LIVING WITH ALCOHOLISM

LIVING WITH ALCOHOLISM

by Elizabeth D. Whitney

BEACON PRESS   BOSTON

For those who seek the truth about alcoholism,
and graciously learn to live with their findings,
this book is dedicated.

ACKNOWLEDGMENTS

I AM SURE that many of the people who have helped me on occasions during the past twenty years as the material for this book was accumulated are unaware of the extent to which they have helped. However, I would like to thank all of these good friends and particularly those who have so constantly encouraged me to share my knowledge, interest, and feelings about alcoholism with others.

In my preparation of this book, Lester Allen, Sr., has given unstintingly of his professional knowledge and skills. Then, there are the officers of the Greater Boston Council of Alcoholism, who have been most generous in urging me to write as I learned from experience while pioneering in many of our initial programs as the executive director of the organization. Among them I list with gratitude Arthur T. Lyman, Charles L. Powers, Herbert Braman, Howard Leavitt, David Landau, M.D., Walter Muther, and Professor Livingston Hall.

I am also grateful to a number of friends who read the manuscript and gave me their frank criticisms: the Reverend Joseph Kellerman; Kenneth Rouse, whose writings have commanded wide attention; Charles Frazier, of Christopher D. Smithers Foundation, whose technical booklets are in international use; and to D. Bruce Mansfield, President of Ohio Edison, who painstakingly put his page-by-page criticism on tape for me to study for purposes of thought and clarity of passages.

E.D.W.

CONTENTS

~~~~~~

CHAPTER 1

EXPLANATION OF ALCOHOLISM

ALCOHOL IS SO MUCH a part of human society that only three small racial groups failed to discover this potent liquid for themselves. The Australian aborigines, the natives of Tierra del Fuego, and the Eskimos had to wait for the coming of the white men to learn about potable alcohol. Consequently, of the world's billions only a few thousand people were in ignorance of the substance and lived for uncounted centuries detached from the pleasures and pain of the mysterious beverage.

Pleasure there is in this fascinating substance. A single ounce will relax the taut and troubled individual strained by competitive living in our tightly wound-up world. Aches and pains that remind mankind of their mortality temporarily disappear. Anxieties are dissolved in a glow of confidence. A relaxed feeling of warm well-being pervades the body. The no-sayers of the mind — the inhibitions — take time off, and the body responds accordingly.

Congeniality blooms even among strangers as the arid distrust of man for man is moistened with alcohol. Individuals in whom shyness is at once a protection from bruises of the ego and an agonizing isolation lower their guard and reveal themselves momentarily as they find fellowship after a few drinks.

Within the limits of individual toleration, alcohol works well as a social lubricant. But, when used as a reinforcement in discussion of more serious matters, it has serious defects which should be taken into consideration. While seeming to enhance one's mental agility and body coordination, it actually affects judgment and has immediate response as an anaesthetic on the motor centers of the brain. Its certain action varies with individuals, but one must note that the original name *Al kool* is the Arabic word for subtle.

There is no denying the subtle ways in which people are deceived by the euphoria caused by alcohol, which leads them to believe they can do very much more than they are capable of doing. They feel, under the influence of alcohol, that they shine in conversation, excel in repartee, are insatiable in lovemaking, and that they can perform prodigies of comedy, strength, skill, and creativity.

Alcohol, the simple elixir of conviviality, becomes the tincture of supermen. Because the action of alcohol impairs judgment, the unwary accept the strange alteration in their thinking as actuality. They have been permitted to peek through the door of escape at the deceitfully pleasant prospects beyond.

An uncomplicated social drinker accepts this glimpse as a pleasant unreality, a mirage. The compulsive drinker, beguiled by the total euphoria of alcohol's depressing effect, believes this mirage is reality. And here is the distinction between attitudes of casual users of alcohol and the habituated, compulsive drinkers, who, fortunately, are in the minority.

So compelling is the compulsive users' belief in the reality of their experience with alcohol that they will not accept proof of their behavior from well-meaning people who may seek to intervene. They are unable to accept that alcohol is faithless to those who love it most or that the favors of alcohol are lethal to those who, through some psychobiochemical abnormality, are vulnerable to alcohol's addictive effect.

There are sound grounds for estimating the frequency of alcoholism among social drinkers. It varies from community to community because of environmental and cultural factors in the lives of users of alcohol. In the United States, roughly 43 percent of the total population uses alcohol as a beverage, in quantities ranging from a drink or two on festive occasions, or a drink or two every day, to the extreme of constant use during waking hours. A two-year survey of American drinking practices by Dr. Ira H. Cisin of George Washington University was reported recently to the American Association for the Advancement of Science.* The majority of Americans over the age of eighteen are included among those who drink socially. The population over eighteen, it was learned by the study, contains about one third who are abstainers, about one half who are moderate drinkers, and about one ninth who are excessive drinkers. Not all of the latter are alcoholics, but a frightening fifty percent of that ninth of the adult population are in one stage or another of alcoholism.

Estimation of the total number of alcoholics in the United States depends upon many variables, ranging from deaths certified due to alcoholism to those who die with such complications as cirrhosis of the liver, gastritis, polyneuritis, and nutritional diseases of several varieties. The latest estimate based on a U.S. population of 200 millions is in excess of 6,500,000 alcoholics. The American Medical Association has estimated as high as 10,000,000.†

Anyone seeking to persuade an alcoholic to face up to the facts will almost immediately become involved in a wearying debate on semantics. One gets a peremptory challenge to

* Meeting, American Association for Advancement of Science, Washington, D.C., Dec. 26, 1966.
  † National Council on Alcoholism.

define alcoholism – to spell out what alcoholism is. What is it? What causes it?

It is quite obvious that alcohol isn't the sole cause of alcoholism. If it were, the national figures would include all who use alcohol. Alcoholism is certainly marked by excessive use of the chemical, but excessive use does not lead inevitably to alcoholism. It merely raises the odds against invulnerability, for there are many heavy drinkers who are not alcoholics inasmuch as they not only have control of their intake but also have ability to abstain.

The theory has been advanced by such distinguished investigators as the late Dr. E. M. Jellinek that there are some men and women who have a constitutional defect, either cellular or psychological, that provides a host favorable to the onset of alcoholism. Physiological theories have found some corroboration in the studies of the role of enzymes and coenzymes in metabolism of alcohol. It has been established that alcoholics do not metabolize alcohol as effectively as nonalcoholics. A study at Harvard Medical School, for example, established that there is a significant difference in the amount of alcohol dehydrogenase produced by the livers of alcoholics as compared to that produced by nonalcoholics. Alcoholism can be recognized by the kind of withdrawal symptoms experienced by persons whose systems do not function normally in metabolizing alcohol. The alcoholic drinking episode is triggered by a high blood-alcohol level sustained over a variable period of time, but the blood-alcohol level has to be elevated in order for the compulsive drinking to begin.

A half century ago it was easy to find medical authority in agreement that alcoholism was hereditary. Scientific investigation has proved this incorrect. It is true that the normal expectancy of alcoholism in children of alcoholics may be as high as twenty-five percent, compared with a normal expectancy of two or three percent in the general population.

But, it is the consensus of investigators that it isn't the arrangement of inherited genes that accounts for the difference, but that environmental factors dispose the children of alcoholics to use alcohol as their alcoholic parent or parents have used it to manage emotional problems. The child chooses the escape route of the parent, researchers believe, and genetics are held blameless. The excessive use of alcohol by the children of alcoholic parents simply exposes them to the risks of excessive drinking so that a larger percentage of people with a family history of excessive use of alcohol are vulnerable.

In recent studies it has been determined that the ways in which parents use alcohol have a profound effect on the drinking behavior of their children. The drinking behavior of an adult faithfully reflects not only the customary home use of alcohol, but also mirrors the cultural factors surrounding the individual. Those denied any experience with the effects of alcoholic beverages tend to have a desire to experiment with it to find out what they are missing. Those who have observed hard drinking at home find justification for their own hard drinking. Those taught from early childhood that moderate use is acceptable as a ceremonial, ritual, or dietary supplement tend to have very low rates of alcoholism. Americans of Chinese, Italian, or Jewish descent show low rates of alcoholism until they adopt the hard drinking ways of American social drinking, and then their cultural buffer seems inadequate and they show higher rates of alcoholism. In the United States, the highest rates are found among ethnic groups whose attitudes towards drinking are more permissive, who do not regard drunkenness as reprehensible, and who have a cultural history of heavy drinking. Swedes, Irish, English, French, and so-called Yankees, all of whom have records of heavy drinking going back several centuries, are very vulnerable to alcoholism. They did not inherit a tendency to alcoholism, however, but they did inherit a

drinking culture which by any standard would be called
excessive. Excessive drinking is one of the necessary factors in
the development of alcoholism.

One rule of thumb yields almost instant determination of
a people's vulnerability to alcoholism. Examine the ethnic
humor. If people laugh at drunken behavior or think drunken
behavior is funny, they lack strong cultural buffers against
alcoholism.

Yet, these generalities about incidence of alcoholism do not
satisfy alcoholics who are more interested in finding reasons
why they should continue to drink, rather than why they
should stop.

Step-by-step examination of the gradualness of involvement in alcoholism may be more helpful as motivation to
undergo treatment. The symptoms of alcoholism do not adhere to a prearranged sequence. They are usually observed
in clusters of symptoms. Acceptance of the clustered symptoms by alcoholics is not always immediate or without in-
cident. It is scarcely helpful to be able to recognize beyond
dispute alcoholic symptoms in others. It is more important
for the alcoholic to recognize and accept the inescapable facts
of alcoholism.

The first symptom is that of denial — denial that a drinking problem exists and resentment at the very sound of the
word alcoholic, which is a constant irritant to those who have
been betrayed by their false friend, alcohol. At one time,
early in the movement for the recognition of alcoholism as a
disease, an effort was made to avoid the use of the words
alcoholic and alcoholism and call the whole thing problem
drinking. Some people proposed calling it Jellinek's disease,
as leprosy has been called Hansen's disease. Choosing a more
acceptable name, however, might prove a balm for the feelings of alcoholics, but no truly descriptive substitute for
alcoholic or alcoholism has been found. Concern about excessive use of alcohol by the majority of drinkers is the basis

for feelings of guilt and ignorance of what alcohol does to produce the desired euphoria. It is a rare person who isn't more or less defensive about use of alcohol. The ancient traditions of drinking are no longer valid. Men once took oaths of trust and fealty by mingling their blood, and this barbarous custom found a shared cup of wine a more acceptable substitute. The blood oath gave way to the ritual of sealing a pact or a contract with a shared alcoholic drink, usually wine. Finally the shibboleth emerged that a person who refused to drink with others was not to be trusted. In sum, alcohol is served by a vast secret society, following the rituals of our drinking ancestors, sharing their feudal superstitions, and meekly accepting all the attitudes and beliefs about drinking which have been demonstrated to be scientifically inaccurate.

Does a shared drink make anyone more trustworthy? Is alcohol a stimulant? Is alcohol good for all the ills man's flesh is heir to? Does alcohol warm the frostbitten wayfarer? Does alcohol improve one's performance? Is alcohol an aphrodisiac? The answer to all these questions is "no," but the majority of people believe it to be "yes."

As an anaesthetic and depressant, alcohol is the key to self-deception. It seems to do all the things mentioned in the foregoing questions because it impairs judgment, releases inhibitions, and gives the illusion of warmth and well-being. Mankind, born to hardship and, in Thoreau's magnificent phrase, "living lives of quiet desperation," accepts alcohol for what it seems to do to obtain for them a feeling of well-being, sweeping aside consideration of what it does to them.

The major hurdle an alcoholic must surmount is inward and private acceptance of the fact that the sickness, despite all his rationalizations, has happened and that it will be with him forevermore. The facts cannot be altered by evasion of the words alcoholism and alcoholic. Denial merely prolongs the suffering.

The anatomy of denial is based on a nagging resentment that alcoholics feel about the use of the words in their presence, on a conscious avoidance of the use of the words or even of discussing the subject, and, finally, on an elaborate network of rationalizations to account for sensitivity of this kind and, more particularly, of any criticism of drinking behavior. This sensitivity is usually experienced very early in the game, while the individual is drinking only occasionally to get relief from anxiety, timidity, tension, frustration, fear, or whatever problem handicaps him and will dissolve in alcohol.

In the most prevalent type of alcoholism, the kind afflicting ninety percent of American alcoholics, there occurs in this beginning phase the cruelest deception of all, a substantial increase in one's tolerance for alcohol. This fits perfectly into our cultural situation in which males strive to appear more manly and virile, and women strive to be more attractive and acceptable as companions for males.

The prealcoholic man, whose tissue tolerance for alcohol has increased, finds in a heavy drinking society some satisfaction at being able to drink others under the table. The woman whose tolerance for alcohol increases is often secretly proud that she, unlike her more vulnerable sisters, doesn't get her lipstick smeared all over her face or commit the social lapse of being unbecomingly drunk in public. This increased tissue tolerance makes it necessary for prealcoholic drinkers to drink more to achieve the same degree of the much-prized euphoria that others achieve on less.

At about this point in the development of the disease the affected individual experiences the first warning from the brain that something is wrong in the way he drinks and the way he metabolizes alcohol. It is as if the brain asks, "Is this the way you want to escape?" and shuts off the memory in the first episode of alcohol amnesia. The first of many blackouts — or attacks of alcohol amnesia — may be passed off with a laugh. Most people who experience their first blackout are often not aware of what has happened. They hear from friends what they did or said and have no recollection of doing a balancing act on the back of a sofa or reciting the funny vulgar poem. It is all a blank to the alcoholic.

A blackout then, quite simply, is alcoholic amnesia. The brain, which is kept functioning by a supply of blood containing a blend of healthy ingredients, reacts to the heightened blood-alcohol level. The memory function shuts down temporarily while the brain works to restore itself and rid itself of the alcohol. Until the blood-alcohol level drops and the memory function is restored, the individual experiences a blackout or alcoholic amnesia which may last hours, minutes, or days, depending upon the continuance of alcohol intake.

The first blackout is a warning. The second blackout is the first alarm. Succeeding blackouts are confirmation of deep trouble. Alcoholism has gained a foothold in the mind and body of the unfortunate alcoholic. At this point it is fairly simple to take the only effective action to halt the inroads of alcoholism — giving up alcohol permanently. But few people heed the warning, the alarm, or the confirmation of their trouble.

They have moved into the first serious phase of alcoholism — the increased dependence on alcohol and covert drinking in one's social group. Covert drinking works this way: before joining the social group for the rites of companionship and fellowship great care is taken to put down a firm alcoholic foundation just in case the host or the bartender doesn't serve drinks fast enough or, worse, the party turns out to have a very limited supply of liquor.

Such ghastly misadventures the alcoholic can avoid by recourse to a flask, a stashed-away pint, or by volunteering to be the bartender. In the latter case the bartender always takes care of himself first. If someone in the social group has made a nasty crack about the alcoholic's overt drinking behavior the alcoholic usually exercises extreme care in showing any preoccupation with alcohol. It is always possible for the alcoholic to propose having a drink or to prolong the drinking or to challenge the manliness and strength of drinking companions without attracting unfavorable attention. In most cases it is simple for an alcoholic in the ascending stage of alcohol toleration to drink everyone under the table. Social intimates would scarcely criticize their peer.

Yet, it is usually at this stage of development of alcoholism that an alcoholic experiences the first twinges of inner feelings of guilt, having been unable by every imaginable kind of rationalization to account for the fact that his drinking behavior is not at all like that of the nonalcoholics. He cannot conceal from himself that when he drinks he undergoes a personality change that is noticed by others. It is at this time that he suspects that he is an alcoholic and that his inability to stop drinking is due to alcoholism.

As their drinking personalities begin to overlap their sober personalities, alcoholics experience increased blackouts — those shattering memory lapses during which they walk, they talk, they appear normal but are, in fact, memoryless.

To conceal their desperate dependency on alcohol, they create what has been called an alibi system, a sort of monologue of excuses to account for their drinking which has universal application to family, friends, colleagues, fellow workers, anyone who may do a double take when the alcoholic is encountered downing an eye-opener on the way to the job or lunching on three double martinis and a glass of milk. It is impossible to go through all the highly imaginative alibis alcoholics utilize, which they may derive from the latent creativity that is frequently encountered in alcoholics.

Not all alcoholics show grandiose and aggressive behavior, but at about this stage of alcoholism, when they are feeling remorseful and then, after a few drinks, elated, they tend to make sweeping gestures, sweeping claims, sweeping largesse. Set up drinks for the house. Borrow a couple of thousand until next Thursday. Be my guest; just charge it to me. This grandiosity is amusing and pitiful. It is the alcoholic's effort to buy understanding and tolerance. Please ignore my drinking behavior because I am really a fine, generous, successful person.

Now come the efforts to control the drinking: the endless litany of remorse, promises to do better, resolutions, pledges, all ending in the same way — more drinking. And the drinking ends in withdrawal symptoms — tremors, shakes, and the feeling that unless they get a drink they will come unglued.

Tragically, the male alcoholic, proud of his ability to put away liquor and never show it, loses even that pitiful distinction. Suddenly, almost overnight, his tolerance for alcohol has reversed. He now gets drunk on less and less liquor. The two-bottle braggart has become a two-drink drunk.

In this crucial phase, there begins the disintegration of the orderly world maintained by the alcoholic in spite of the compulsive drinking. Work and money troubles loom large at this stage. The alcoholic, in one of his spasms of good resolutions, may try to run away from his problem — go somewhere else and leave alcoholism behind. This is called geographical escape. If he tries geographical escape he may leave behind carping family members, lukewarm friends, coteries of hard-drinking companions, and all the memories of painful broken promises. Nevertheless, alcoholism goes along with him as an unshakable Old Man of the Sea, not to be thrown off by time or distance.

Even here rationalizations are employed to account for flight to a new place, to mingle with new people. The unreasonable resentments of an alcoholic include placing blame upon his old social group. He thinks they rejected him not because of his drinking behavior, which made them in their own frame of reference feel guilty about drinking, but be-

cause he showed them all up as a he-man and a sturdy
drinker. He feels he has not been rejected by them: he has
simply dropped them and found himself some really competitive company with which to drink, men and women who will
not criticize his drinking behavior because their own cannot
bear the scrutiny of anyone familiar with the phases of alcoholism.

Now, in geographical escape, he is leaving all that behind.
He is alone and a prey of memory. The loneliness and isolation are too much to bear in a strange place. The alcoholic
has to have a little drink for solace, then another and still
another. The cycle begins all over again, only this time he has
severe psychological and physiological reactions. The drinking bouts last longer. The withdrawal symptoms are more
severe. The people with whom he drinks are now inferior to
him, and he fears that a moral deterioration has set in.

Performance on the new job, if he has one, suffers from
impaired thinking. Rumors reach the new employers, who
notice that he is unable to initiate action without alcohol and
that his life seems completely oriented to alcohol intake.

Indefinable fears now creep into all his thinking. He is
obsessed by drinking. He struggles to alibi himself with those
who matter to him, but he has just run out of alibis. Somewhere in the deep of night, when he hopes there will not be
another dawn, he remembers prayers of childhood. He has
amorphous spiritual feelings that ameliorate his profound
conviction of unworthiness. In this crisis comes the admission
that liquor has beaten him. He is no longer the master. His
every tissue and fibre is strung on a single hook — alcohol.

The foregoing outline of the course of alcoholism, from its
forerunning signs to its chronic stage and through the crucial
phases in between, does not necessarily describe the experience of every alcoholic in this sequence. The symptoms may
be clustered out of sequence. Some may not try geographical
escape in the sense that they leave home and go elsewhere.

But, while actually living at home, they may have rejected everything that a home means to an individual. Home may become a place to go when spiritually and physically exhausted, and the people there may become the objects of unreasonable resentment because they love and care and cannot help, because of ignorance of the ways of alcoholism.

"No one understands," the alcoholic cries. "No one knows how I suffer."

The loneliness and isolation and lack of understanding experienced by an alcoholic are the fault of our society, which prefers ignorance to knowledge of alcoholism.

And most ignorant of all are the alcoholics, who, in overwhelming majority, have to be taught as they struggle for recovery how their bodies utilize and metabolize alcohol. And they have to learn that while alcohol may be a friend to some, an alcoholic cannot use a friend like that.

Care and caution in the use of alcohol are manifest in the drinking behavior of so-called social drinkers who avoid intoxication.

A short step, even one additional drink, away from that kind of alcohol use is the phase of intoxication marked by impaired judgment, relaxing of inhibitions, loud conversation, vulgarity, boasting, spendthrift behavior, making passes at the opposite sex, and impairment of vision.

A very little way beyond that is drunkenness in which hostility, combativeness, staggering, excessive emotion, violence, nausea, loss of coordination, sweating, flushing, and skin rash appear.

Upon going into the second stage of loss of judgmental ability, the user of alcohol has no effective control over the problem of drinking behavior. Getting drunk (with loss of consciousness, dilation of pupils, inability to control bladder or bowels, and lowering of body temperature as vital processes slow down) is closer to death than social users of alcohol care to go; and so the social drinker rarely experiences this advanced phase of intoxication. Alcoholics, however, lacking the ability to control habituation, may experience these dangerous symptoms of excess many times.

The sources of much misunderstanding about treatment of alcoholism is the fine distinction between the incurable aspects of alcoholism and recovery from the adverse effects of alcoholism through complete abstinence.

There is no cure for alcoholism, even though thousands of people live normally without alcohol. To say that a person is "cured" of alcoholism indicates to many persons that the alcoholic can drink safely again without relapsing. The fact is that no individual, once afflicted with alcoholism, can be given any assurance that there will be no relapse if even a very moderate amount of alcohol is taken.

This is the point where a line must be drawn if alcoholics who have recovered from their sickness are to be secure. As long as an alcoholic does not drink at all (one drink is too many) he is considered to be a recovered alcoholic but, nevertheless, an alcoholic. The comparison of alcoholism with tuberculosis or diabetes is relevant to the alcoholic's problem. Under certain conditions both tubercular and diabetic people will relapse and suffer a recurrence of their acute symptoms. It is the same with alcoholics. Because of the unfortunate connotation of the word "arrest" one never refers to an alcoholic as an arrested alcoholic, even though that is a more precise definition of the condition of recovery.

It is difficult for the alcoholic individual to achieve acceptance of the fact that there is no cure for alcoholism, and it is almost as difficult for the nonalcoholic person to understand this fact.

The person who explains that he does not drink because he is an alcoholic is explaining recovery the only way it can be explained in the light of present medical knowledge.

CHAPTER 2

~~~~~~

DRINKING BEHAVIOR —
THE ACTUALITY

QUITE BY CHANCE a singular sameness in the early drinking experience of a group of male alcoholics developed in a group counseling session. The men, all aged between 38 and 40, were swapping drinking experiences. Out of the good-humored banter about drinking episodes that ranged from tragic to ridiculous, it seemed that a pattern developed.

The group happened to be in the age group of young men drafted or volunteered in the armed services in the years between 1940 and 1945. Indeed, their memorable drinking experiences all seemed to revolve around drinking experiences while they were in the Army, Navy, Air Force, Coast Guard, or Marines.*

The tales they told were often generously larded with exaggerated details, but as they told the stories it was apparent that to each one the most memorable drinking experiences had happened when they were either in their late teens or very early twenties.

"I was in an ordnance company on Tinian. We scrounged a lot of whiskey from a Seabee outfit, and we got some captured Japanese beer. Five of us stayed drunk for a week."

* Study by Consulting and Guidance Service 1967.

"We were on the Murmansk run. You could get sent to the bottom any time. But we had some torpedo juice, and when we were at general quarters for a couple of days at a time going around the North Cape no one paid much attention if you staggered a little because we were all blind with fatigue. But did that booze make it easier! We all stopped being tensed-up waiting for a torpedo to slam into us."

"I had a sergeant who was a wonder at finding booze. We got into an Italian farmyard one time and he smelled out some buried stuff — that Italian grappa — buried under a big stack of straw. I forgot what it was like to be sober until I got hit in the leg and wound up in the hospital at Caserta."

"We were flying against the oil fields in Rumania — a tough, long, exhausting run out of the North African fields, and lots of flak when you got there. So, we would stay plastered from the time we got back safe from Ploesti until we had to make another run, but it added up to two or three days of steady drinking — maybe a quart of whiskey a day."

"The Marines didn't get much of the gravy. We were first wave troops, going into the beach, and when it was secured we were often pulled out. So, between landings we went into rest areas, and, boy, I got a couple of gallons of cocoanut milk brandy — that's fermented cocoanut juice, distilled by the Seabees — and believe me, my buddy and me, we could practically run up one of those palm trees."

These and similar yarns had one thing in common — all were about excessive drinking experiences; all happened in late teens and early twenties, and a little probing disclosed that it was this pattern of excessive drinking that the group had taken back to civilian life when they were discharged. One of the group summed up the reaction of the folks at home.

"My mother watched me spend my bonus money on booze, and one night she said she gave the Army a nice young American boy, and they sent her back a drunk. It was kind of rough but she had a point. I didn't drink like that before I was drafted."

The first clue to the meaning of this pattern of drinking behavior came from the longitudinal study of alcoholics conducted by Dr. William McCord at Harvard School of Sociology and based on the Cambridge-Somerville Youth Study. It showed that early drinking experiences copied the drinking behavior of peer figures and also conformed to the socially acceptable behavior of the group. In the case of the veterans, they had established patterns of excessive drinking during their war service years, when they were of a most plastic and impressionable age. They took this excessive drinking pattern back to civilian life with them, and, because of the high ratio of excessive drinking in their age group, problems of alcoholism were not identified until they were out of control and in the chronic stage.

Working from this clue, all the men in that age bracket who were admitted to the consultation and guidance service for help with an alcoholic problem were specifically interviewed about their most memorable drinking experience and, in the case of all the veterans who turned up in the sample, their most memorable drinking experience had been a drinking episode when they were very young men, away from home, in the frantic environment of wartime service in one of the fighting forces.

This means of studying wartime drinking behavior also applied to women who had been in active services in the Wacs, the Waafs, the Waves, and the Red Cross and who had later developed drinking problems. But, in the case of the women, the excessive drinking episodes while in service were not as frequent, although in many cases they were equally bizarre. The women war veterans showed most of their drinking problems to be emotional problems.

Yet, it is now manifest that early drinking behavior yields many clues to the eventual crucial and chronic stages of alcoholism. One can now almost predict the type of alcoholism that will beset the individual in later years if one has enough of the early drinking history on which to base a fair judgment.

The late Professor E. M. Jellinek, as chairman of the World Health Organization Committee on Alcoholism, undertook the task of classifying the various types of alcoholism because the studies at the Yale School of Alcohol Studies had indicated that alcoholism was a disease that could not be clearly defined by a single set of symptoms. As a biostatistician, Dr. Jellinek had detected cultural, anthropological, and economic factors affecting the prevalence of the disease in various ethnic groups. He established in his great work, *The Disease Concept of Alcoholism* (published by the Christopher D. Smithers Foundation), that certain geographical areas, which sometimes overlap national boundaries, develop types of alcoholism peculiar to their cultures. The types are most easily recognized by laymen in the case of gamma alcoholism, which is by far the most common type of alcoholism encountered in the United States and Canada, and delta alcoholism, the type affecting the vast majority of wine-drinking Frenchmen. The types are listed in Table 1 with

TABLE 1

Five Types of Alcoholism

ALPHA ALCOHOLICS
  Retain ability to abstain
  Rely on alcohol to relieve body and emotional pain
  Do not adhere to acceptable social drinking patterns
  Have damage to interpersonal relations
  Experience no withdrawal symptoms
  May continue 30 or 40 years or
  May develop into gamma alcoholics

BETA ALCOHOLICS

   Have no physical or psychological dependence

   Suffer complications: gastritis, cirrhosis of the liver, polyneuritis, nutritional diseases, curtailed lifespan

   Experience impairment of family finances, lowered productivity, but no withdrawal symptoms

   May develop into Gamma alcoholics

GAMMA ALCOHOLICS

   Increased tissue tolerance (drink more in order to achieve the euphoria that others experience with less)

   Cells adapt to metabolize increased amounts of alcohol

   Peak drinking ability reverses; they get drunk on less and less liquor

   Loss of control; withdrawal symptoms; physical dependence (craving); behavior changes

   Retain some ability to abstain at intervals

DELTA ALCOHOLICS

   May show some of the characteristics of gamma alcoholism: increased tissue tolerance, adaptive cell metabolism, withdrawal symptoms and craving

   Unable to abstain even for a day

   Can control the amount they drink

   Seldom seen in the United States; common in France as inveterate wine drinkers

   Go into withdrawal symptoms if they try to abstain

EPSILON ALCOHOLICS

   Periodic drinkers, differing from the pseudoperiodic drinkers who are classed as gamma alcoholics

   Called "alcoolisation" by the French, rarely seen in the United States

the signs most often recognized by professional therapists.

   The five listed types of alcoholism are considered diseases. Alpha and beta alcoholism are shown to be forerunning types which may lead into gamma alcoholism, even though those who do not become gamma alcoholics experience serious diseases resulting from their excessive drinking. Gamma and delta alcoholism, however, are considered to have physiopathological changes which constitute a true disease classification.

If early drinking patterns violate accepted social rules as to the appropriate or acceptable time, place, amount, and effect of drinking, but do not show loss of control or, more appropriately, inability to abstain from drinking, one cannot declare beyond doubt that the person showing those reactions to drinking is an alcoholic. In some cases the individual drinks to relieve bodily or mental stress, and the resultant behavior may result in a loss of friendly and close drinking companions, in adverse effects on the family budget, debts, absenteeism from work, inefficiency, and quarrelsome interpersonal relations. But, in and of themselves, these patterns prove nothing more than the fact that the individual has a drinking problem, that he is what has been called a dependent drinker. But, unless signs of a progressive process are present, unless there are severe withdrawal symptoms, this type of trouble does not develop into addiction drinking. It has been classified by Jellinek as alpha alcoholism.

Some people can go along for thirty or forty years with this kind of drinking trouble, but, unless it develops into an addiction type of alcoholism, it lacks the destructiveness of progressive symptoms. Such dependent drinkers can stop drinking when they choose or when the physical and mental stresses make no demands for the euphoria of alcohol.

Al was an alpha type drinker. When he dropped in at the favorite bar of his fellow workers, he would inevitably get argumentative. No one really liked to drink with him, but, as Al said, "Just start an argument and I'll take the other side." He was frequently at odds with the boss, and the boss threatened any number of times to fire him. Al didn't drink on the job, nor did he go on benders. He was very opinionated and, when he drank at home, displayed the same ungracious behavior that he did with his fellow workers. The bartender at the "Wee Drop" knew a lot of drinkers like Al and he gave them little time.

"When they get a drink or two they have big mouths," the bartender said. "But they drink because they want to, not because they have to." Al was also a prankster. His idea of a good joke was to drop a rubber frog into a friend's beer. His wife had all his jokes tried on her at least once. She didn't think Al was much of a comedian, not even the day a furniture van stopped at the house and took away the parlor set and Al explained it was just a gag. It was such a joke that the furniture company didn't bring the set back until he had paid up three months' installments.

While his behavior outraged social conventions, Al was more a rebel than an alcoholic drinker. He went on the wagon from time to time, sometimes for as long as six months. Eventually, he lost his job as an automobile assembler, borrowed enough money to hire a garage, and went into the automobile repair business. The responsibility of running his own business, plus the opportunity to assert himself as an expert on what goes on in an automobile inwards without getting an argument from a customer, resulted in his giving up drinking, except for a ceremonial glass at weddings, Kiwanis club annual dinners, and similar events. He was not an alcoholic — merely a misfit in the drinking milieu in which he found himself.

But those who think that they, like Al, are misunderstood dependent drinkers and not alcoholics with a compulsive need to drink, may be interested in the experience of Joe.

Joe was an automobile dealer. Most of his friends, when he was drinking, sought to avoid getting into arguments or even raising a controversial subject. Joe's gambit, or what used to be called one-upmanship, was the extremely masculine stance. Joe was a real he-man. He said so. He delighted in not only arguing and drinking, but also in putting his drinking companions under the table and even taking them home in the demonstrator car. People said that they didn't understand Joe. When he was selling automobiles and not drinking he was described as "a very sweet guy," but when he was drinking he was described generally as "a stinking monster."

He had all of Al's trouble with alcohol, ranging from loss of friends to unmanageable debts, but he had what Al didn't have — an acquired tissue tolerance for alcohol. Where Al would get to feeling reasonably "high" on three or four drinks, it took at least half a dozen before Joe even got started. It seemed that as Joe got older he could drink not less, but more and more. But he had personality changes while he was drinking and, unknown to others, his cells, used to being washed by blood with an 0.10% blood-alcohol, had adapted to metabolizing extra amounts of alcohol only at the price of severe withdrawal symptoms and a distinct craving for more alcohol. With his physical dependence on alcohol, he paid the price of his long psychological dependence on the feelings of well-being that alcohol gave to him. With Joe the use of alcohol was an addiction.

Let Charley serve to demonstrate the beta type of alcoholism. Charley was a traveling salesman, accustomed to stop in a different town and sleep in a different bed every night. During the day he was usually too busy to stop for a regular and proper meal. He might stop at a roadside stand, one that served liquor, and lunch on a dry martini and a glass of milk or three beers and a sandwich or a piece of pie followed by a stinger. Most of his customers liked a drink when placing an order with Charley. So, by the time he checked into a motel, he had a fairly high blood level of alcohol. Before going to bed he would have a few drinks in the cocktail lounge. The time came when Charley's entertainment bill was bigger than his gasoline bill, and he moved on to another sales job and, later, still another. They said of Charley that he was a top-notch salesman, if you could afford his entertainment bills. There came the time in Tennessee when he ran into an emergency situation. All the motel proprietor had on hand for sale was "white lightning," sold in a Mason jar. Charley liked his Tennessee calls after that, until he developed polyneuritis and some very detailed symptoms of cirrhosis of the liver. He also had developed a divorce, alimony payments, child-support payments, and a feeling that home was anywhere he could settle down for a dozen or so drinks. Charley finally lost his last job and soon after that he died in the hospital maintained by the fraternal order to which he had belonged for the reason that it usually had a clubhouse with a bar in all the towns in the territories he covered. Charley's type of alcoholism can develop into addictive gamma type alcoholism, too, but Charley didn't give it a chance. The poor diet and the excessive drinking killed him before addictive alcoholism could develop. Charley had a noteworthy characteristic. "I could always tell when old Charley had a skinful," said one of his customers. "He walked like he was stepping from egg to egg along a sidewalk full of eggs, almost like he was dancing."

Emile was a French-Canadian millhand, expert at setting up Jacquard looms. He had started to drink when he was a mere infant and his family served him wine and water at meals. When Emile got up in the morning, he had some wine with a little hot water. He stopped on the way to work and had a hasty glass or two of ordinary wine. At lunch hour he tugged at a Thermos bottle filled with wine. And a couple of times on the way home to dinner he stopped off to have an aperitif. After dinner he had a brandy. To be explicit, Emile drank as inveterate French drinkers imbibe, steadily throughout his waking hours, a total intake which keeps the blood-alcohol level as high as 0.10%, hitting a peak at bedtime of perhaps 0.15%. Emile drank mostly wines and aperitifs, shunning fortified wines and all liquors except brandy.

He wasn't happy, but he wasn't quarrelsome either. He existed in a sort of foggy glow, which, after a time, fellow workers accepted as his natural state. They would have been astounded to be told that Emile was an alcoholic, for he never staggered, he never showed hostility to others, and his drinking was controlled in the sense that he never drank more or less — always about the same amount every day. The fact was that Emile had lost the physiological and psychological abilities to stop drinking. He had to keep on, as an accident in which he was involved showed. The accident did not happen at his work. In fact, it should be emphasized that alcoholics of every type generally show a lower accident rate when they become fully cognizant of their dependence on alcohol — their accident rate is generally lower than that of nonalcoholics, who may drink on the job.* The explanation is that alcoholics working in situations where accidents may happen, or driving automobiles, or in any other hazardous situation, slow down and exercise greater care because they are aware that accidents might expose their dependency on alcohol.

In Emile's case his automobile was struck by a truck on his way home from work, and he was taken to a hospital, unconscious, with compound fractures of his left leg and left arm. He awoke in a traction frame after the breaks had been set, and almost immediately he went into withdrawal symptoms. His alcoholism had never been put to such a test because he had always maintained a blood-alcohol level that prevented withdrawal symptoms.

This type, delta alcoholism, which is the name that Dr. Jellinek gave to Emile's type, is not very common in the United States because America is not a wine-drinking land. France, however, sees a very great percentage of the world's sufferers from delta alcoholism. To a certain extent, Switzer-

* Harrison M. Trice, N.Y., School of Industrial Relations, Cornell University 1960.

land and the Rhine valley areas see a great many examples of this type of alcoholic.

The drinking culture in which it is socially acceptable to sip wine throughout the day, to have aperitifs before meals, and a liqueur after meals, thus keeping the tissues bathed in a fairly high blood-alcohol solution all through the waking hours, does not prevail in all wine-drinking countries. Italy, for example, has a fairly low rate of alcoholism due to the fact that Italians use wine as a food supplement only and have an antipathy against drunkenness.

The French have a word that they use for the wine-soaked individual who has suffered physical and psychological damage from the constant heavy drinking. They call it *alcoolisation*. Many scientists believe that alcoolisation is a terminal or deep chronic phase of delta alcoholism.

In the gray area between alpha alcoholism and delta alcoholism there is a type called epsilon alcoholism, which has not yet been ascribed a place in the alpha, beta, gamma, delta series of drinking behaviors. Jellinek called it epsilon alcoholism.

Tom, the epsilon alcoholic, was a periodic drinker. There had been a time when he was somewhat like an alpha alcoholic in that he drank to relieve body or emotional pain and seemed to suffer no progressive symptoms.

He was a lawyer, and his practice involved him in trial work. He tried cases for other lawyers, and his courtroom appearances were usually brilliant and much admired by other lawyers. His preparation of cases was meticulous, and his cross examinations were masterpieces of functional skill in entrapment of hostile witnesses.

But, at the conclusion of any particularly arduous trial, which happened once or twice a year, Tom would disappear for a couple of weeks. When he returned to his home and his practice, he would be weak, shaken, drawn, and obviously recovering from a bout of illness. It was a long time before his colleagues of the legal profession learned where he went, how he drank, and where he tapered off and regained sobriety. But he wasn't considered by them to be an alcoholic because he refrained from drinking between these periodic drinking episodes and showed no need for liquor.

Whether the type of alcoholism an individual suffers is any one of the five main species outlined, the fact remains that the use of alcohol has caused damage to the individual and to society. The delta alcoholic cannot abstain from the use of alcohol because his ability to abstain is damaged, but he can control the amounts that he drinks. The gamma alcoholic can go on the water wagon between episodes, and so can the periodic or epsilon alcoholic and the alpha and beta species of compulsive drinker. But they, unlike the delta alcoholic, do not spread their drinking over all their waking hours. Usually they desire the fast action, the shock of strong distilled spirits, the quick euphoria, not the mild pervasive glow of the wine drinker.

Few therapists or counselors in the United States try to make the distinction between one species of alcoholism and another. They simply recognize that alcoholism is damaging the individual and that strict control must be established by the drinker over the use of alcoholic beverages, else the disease will continue in its destructive effects.

It is surprising but true that Alcoholics Anonymous groups rarely see a delta alcoholic. In fact, the fellowship is made up mainly of gamma alcoholics, chiefly because that is the species of alcoholism most prevalent in Anglo-Saxon countries, where AA has its most numerous membership. In fact, Dr. Jellinek remarked that AA "recognizes" gamma alcoholism as alcoholism to the exclusion of all other species. Because the alpha alcoholic resembles the gamma alcoholic in very early phases of alcoholism, there are certainly quite a few alpha alcoholics who have recovered in AA under the discipline which has proved so effective for gamma alcoholism.

There are certain types of alcoholism not yet classified. One of these is fiesta drinking observed mainly in the primitive parts of South America where natives indulge in drinking bouts as part of a celebration. The intent is to get insensibly drunk and to remain that way for periods of several days. But, when the fiesta is over, the drinking is over until the next fiesta.

There is a tendency of those who are not addicted to alcohol to pass judgments on alcoholics concerning the moral and ethical aspects of compulsive drinking. In a social drinking society, where status symbols are more common than escutcheons, those who can drink in an acceptable social way set themselves above those who cannot. Those who can control their social drinking often proclaim that alcoholism is a self-inflicted disease. They give no weight to the excessive drinking behavior of the entire culture in which their drinking group exists. Nor do they take into account the adaptive cell metabolism that develops in the gamma alcoholic.

If one surveys the whole social drinking scene, one finds that social standards are set mainly by women, and women are far more cruel than men to the members of their own sex who become alcoholics. The drinking customs of males extend back through a changing social structure many, many centuries, and men have a tolerance for those of their sex who cannot cope with alcohol. They may think of the abstainer as peculiar and of the man who cannot drink a great deal as physically "weak," but they are far readier to say of a Skid Row drunk, "There, except for the Grace of God, go I." Women scorn or, worse, pity those of their sisterhood who hide their alcoholic sickness in secret drinking at home or who get drunk in public.

The fact is that very few alcoholics foresee the development of their illness or are even aware of the forerunning signs of alcoholism, simply because of the insidious and subtle preliminary symptoms. Education about alcohol and its effect on the human body is so limited and so circumscribed by the individual bias of the teachers, either in school or at home, that the difference between the abnormal drinker and the social drinker is seldom explored or understood.

At the very least, the forerunning signs of alcoholism and the facts about the way in which the human body metabolizes alcohol should be known to everyone. It is therefore not surprising that the average alcoholic who comes to treatment knows only of the pleasure derived from drinking alcoholic beverages and that this pleasure — if indulged to excess — is paid for with pain. It is the rare alcoholic who can explain how the feeling of well-being comes about. That simple progression from impaired judgment and loosened inhibitions is a mystery to alcoholics. They only know that it does something for them as a solver for all their immediate problems. Tomorrow is another day!

There is an easy test of the depth of any individual's knowledge of alcohol and its effects. Those who call it a stimulant display their ignorance. It is an anaesthetic and a depressant, and always has been. The stories of Al, Joe, and Charley illustrate three of the variations of drinking behavior most often encountered. Joe, the automobile dealer, with his acquired tissue tolerance for alcohol, his personality changes when drinking, and his acute withdrawal symptoms, started out to be only an excessive drinker, but his adaptive cell metabolism triggered alcoholism. Charley might have developed into the same kind of alcoholic as Joe, but his serious nutritional complications killed him before his alcoholism had changed into the gamma type.

It is important to observe that in all three cases, the economic and social damage to them and their families left small distinction between the types of alcoholism they suffered. It is because of this harm done to others, particularly family members, that alcoholism affects the lives of at least ten persons for every alcoholic. If one multiplies the figure 6,500,000 — the estimate of the total number of alcoholics in this country — by ten, it can be understood that over 65,000,000 Americans have a stake in control of this health problem.*

* NCA annual meeting proceedings 1967.

~~~~~~

CHAPTER 3

REWARDS AND RATIONALIZATIONS

FROM THE TIME of earliest primitive societies a system of rewards and rationalizations of extraordinary complexity has grown around group drinking. Perhaps the earliest examples are found in the blood oath of warrior groups. It was a simple step from mingling blood from opened veins in the forearm to taking the oath of brotherhood and fealty by ritual drinking of red wine from a shared cup.

While it may have taken eons for this ritual to develop into other kinds of social and anthropological applications, the end result has been the ritual use of alcohol to mark the most meaningful events in human lives. The end of puberty, the betrothal, the marriage, the business deal, the pledge of friendship, the symbol of mutual trust — all require alcohol to give a more profound meaning to the vast majority of people.

Those who decline to drink with a social group are suspect. Those who refuse to drink with certain individuals declare their hostility. The seasons are hailed with drinking rituals — May wines, bock beers, Bacchic revels. Seasons are also given an alcoholic farewell. Individuals who declare with special emphasis "I'll drink to that" have invoked the most ancient of rationalizations.

Our social drinking society today evolved through all the guilt feelings about drinking, all the convulsive soul searching, all of man's attempts to control the use of alcoholic beverages as well as from the simple fact that alcohol gives a feeling of well-being to its partakers. It is not an accident of history that a materialistic, competitive, social drinking society should develop a system of status seeking and status maintenance in connection with the use of alcoholic beverages. America had been forced to adapt to the drinking cultures of many ethnic groups who emigrated from Europe to a frontier society and who, in the process, developed a heavy drinking social usage of alcohol which could be mitigated only by artificial canons of acceptable drinking behavior.

Our experience with national prohibition is a clear example of cause and effect, action and reaction. The militant temperance movement, itself a reaction against the excessive sale and use of alcoholic beverages, strove for over a century to have a strict prohibition law enacted. After a long struggle fought at local and state levels to forbid sale of liquor, the opportunity was presented during World War I to hook a prohibition law into the idealistic crusade of the "war to end all wars." A national sumptuary law was enacted, and a constitutional amendment was accepted by a majority of the States, forbidding the sale of alcoholic beverages except under ironclad restrictions for use as medicine. It was perhaps ironic that the prohibition amendment did not go into effect until after the end of the conflict and at a time when the American people had emerged from their isolation and were feeling their muscles as a world power. The wreckage of the idealistic crusade and the expansion of the national economy virtually doomed prohibition before it was ever put into operation.

There is no question today that national prohibition wrought incalculable harm in a comparatively unsophisticated body politic. The sumptuary laws forbidding the sale of alcoholic beverages did not really prohibit. By the very laws that forbade them to use alcohol, the great mass of the people were stimulated to sample what was forbidden. The nation experienced its first wave of lawlessness soon after the first months of prohibition, and the situation grew progressively worse. The whiskey rebellions of the nineteenth century seemed mere pranks by comparison.

What were the rewards that made a law-abiding people flout laws and indulge in illegally obtained alcohol and, in the process, tear down the taboos which for centuries had kept women discreetly out of sight in public drinking places?

Anyone who has ever experienced the social usage of alcohol knows the primary answer. As a quick tranquilizer and social lubricant, alcohol is without a peer. It works quickly and effectively. As little as an ounce of a solution that is less than fifty percent alcohol, partaken in any situation, gives the illusion of well-being. The jaded appetite sharpens. The reticent individual is suddenly articulate and outgoing.

The average "normal" person has in the course of reaching emancipation been compelled by social usage to make use of inhibiting controls, little warning signs in the highways of the mind that say "Slow, Caution." But an ounce of alcohol can and does have the effect of flipping down those signs to expose a contrary legend, "Resume Speed." The drinker takes several steps backward towards that primitive past when alcohol acted upon a much more basic set of taboos.

The rewards of alcohol are not all illusory. Some of them are actual. In twentieth century America, anxieties and tensions abound. Alcohol works very well in this instance, although it conditions the individual to greater dependence on the chemical action of alcohol and to too little on objective thinking.

To each user alcohol grants a special set of rose-colored glasses, ground to personal formula. The woman who seeks release from the humdrum, who seeks to be noticed, admired, and pursued as a woman, sees some inner glow in her mirror with even a moderate amount of alcoholic beverage. In her mind's eye, ordinarily so unsparing of her minor defects of looks or character, she sees the person of her dreams. The man engaged in a desperate struggle onward and upward in the social order has dreamed dreams, even as has the woman. A very small quantity of alcohol gives life to those dreams and aspirations. The man may understand completely that it is only the euphoria of liquor that makes dreams seem close to reality, but, nevertheless, it is very much to be desired to have an hour or two in the bright atmosphere of a fantasy world and to get away from the gray, drab, real world.

People with emotional problems are ashamed of this desire for alcohol-induced feelings of well-being. It nullifies that status that they seek. And so rationalizations are adopted to explain the need for quick euphoria. The social drinking group collaborates on such rationalizations. They adopt a code, a set of manners, a ritual to govern the times when they drink together. One of the sternest tenets of the code is never drink alone, a tenet flouted with more and more frequency as the individual falls victim to the rewards and rationalizations surrounding drinking.

Even the lowly Skid Row alcoholic — fortunately a small minority in the vast brotherhood of drinking people — has his drinking code, his drinking ritual, a stylized way of passing the shared bottle, an iron rule of rejection for those who do not share the alcohol available.

From time to time society sets up new drinking rules to serve the needs of a group, be it an ethnic group or a social group. These rules range from the noncondemning behavior of the carousers to severe restrictions on time, place, purpose, and participants in social drinking occasions. The afternoon tea disappears and becomes the cocktail hour. The business lunch is preceded by a couple of cocktails, where once there was little or no drinking in the business community before the predinner cocktail hour. Religious taboos on drinking become modified, changing from the puritanical to the permissive. Women were once barred from public drinking places or sequestered in a back room. Today they drink in public with few restrictions. These cultural factors have not been given the study they require or deserve if we are to understand the cultural climate of our drinking behavior.

Several great American corporations have promulgated rules forbidding executive personnel from signing contracts except at an hour when they are least likely to have indulged in alcohol. The rules were made necessary by experience with disastrous errors of judgment arrived at in business drinking groups with consequent losses to the corporations.

Safety regulations in situations where the lives of others depend upon the good judgment of a single individual also bring about no-drinking rules. But, wherever a set of rules governing drinking are adopted and for whatever purpose, alcoholics will find a rationalization to contravene such rules. Their need is far stronger than their compliance with the code of their particular group.

The rewards and rationalizations of the Skid Row alcoholics are astonishingly simple when subjected to study. Most Skid Row drinkers have experienced loss of a wife, mother, or sweetheart upon whom they have been deeply dependent. Skid Row offers a substitute — the bartender, who is the giver; the policeman, who "mothers" them by protecting them with arrest, shelter, and authority; and employers, who provide menial jobs, which demand neither regularity nor skill and in turn provide the money that makes it possible to return to the bartender and repeat the cycle.

While this statistically unimportant group (three percent of the total number of alcoholics in the United States) displays very simple motivation for excessive drinking, the rewards and rationalizations of men and women alcoholics, as one goes up the economic and social scale, become increasingly complex. Investigators have shied away from "reasons for drinking" because of this complexity of motives and rewards.

Within recent years it has become certain that the ratio of male to female alcoholics is not six to one as early estimates indicated, but closer to three to one and, in some urban social groups, two to one. There are a far larger number of women alcoholics than investigators at first estimated. And by far the greater percentage of them are labeled "respectable" women, which is to say they are wives and mothers, they live in pleasant surroundings, have no apparent problems, but, nevertheless, they have created a problem within their families as they become alcoholics.

Some women say they drank socially to become vivacious. Some report drinking to overcome shyness. Some say they strove to conform to the drinking pattern of their social group and to become popular. Very few report liking the taste of liquor. But virtually all confessed a liking for the effect experienced although many say that the unremitting quest for relief from daily routine did not come until after the big emotional crisis that triggered their compulsive drinking.

The high ratio of drinking women who as alcoholics drink secretly and alone reflects a general attitude shared by women that alcoholism is shameful. The loneliness and boredom of housewifery seems to become critical at about the time children go to school or, even more, when they go away to camp or to college. Women report finding themselves aiming for the cocktail hour when husbands come home to dinner and then aiming for lunch time when they could in good conscience have a drink, and, finally, drinking throughout the day, using the telephone to communicate with others when they were oppressed by a feeling of isolation. In a remarkably frequent number of case histories, one finds the husband or family members pleading with the alcoholic woman not to venture out of the house while drinking and providing her with the liquor to drink so that her addiction would not become known to neighbors and friends. This, of course, with a telephone at her elbow, always available for attacks of telephonitis, is ridiculous. Listen to a few women alcoholics.

"Oh, I felt young and carefree when I drank. I didn't look into mirrors. There were lines around the eyes, you know. But a drink makes me feel young and gay and wanted — that's it. Wanted. I feel that no one wants me."

"After the divorce and the settlement, I thought that I would have many beaus, all wanting to marry me, but it wasn't that way at all. I was left alone, severely alone. I didn't blame the two children, who had been given into my custody, although no man wants a woman with two kids unless he is exceptional. I didn't even have a social life any more, and so I drank at home by myself, put on records and danced by myself . . . ."

"When my daughter went away to college the house was empty. My husband is away all day and out of town on business. I got sick of hen parties and time-wasting things to do. I wanted to feel happy, and a drink helped. It was easy — easy."

"You know what I found out — men are afraid of drunken women. I tried a pickup or two in my drinking days — and the men were afraid — and I was the type who drank until I passed out. Anything could have happened to me, but nothing did. I drank in first-class cocktail lounges, not in dumps. I had two lives — my drinking life and my life as a proper matron out in the suburbs. Either way I felt dreadfully lonely."

This theme of loneliness was stressed over and over again. Loneliness and boredom, youth slipping into the past, fearfulness of the future. Women confessing that while they drank they envied and even hated their daughters for their youth and their easy vivacity. As for drinking occasions, few women needed to search for one.

"I could always find a reason to have a drink," one woman

explained, "I was the first to suggest sweetly to my husband that *he* needed a drink, and I would have a drink with him."

Around this structure of rationalizations twine many, many other complex growths of motivation for drinking. Competition with others — social and economic. Unhappy love affairs. Rebuffs. Plainness. Frustration in a job. Inclusion in a heavy social drinking group. Fatigue. Nervousness. Menopause. Loss of a child. Widowhood. Dependent parents. Liquor self-prescribed as medicine.

In all cases the cultural factors were important, and the drinking code of the social group looms large to women in determining how their drinking pattern develops. The stigma on drunkenness in woman seems to account for most of the drift to secret drinking and to concealment of alcoholic behavior. In the latter case, concealment is almost impossible because we live in a social drinking society and in communities geared to use of the telephone.

The male alcoholic has an extraordinary range of rewards and rationalizations. One might suspect that a great many of them are invented to make their drinking histories sound more interesting. On closer examination, it usually turns out that, rather than minimizing the motivation of their drinking, they haven't been telling half the story. Many men do not always know what they got out of drinking and can only guess at their early involvement in alcoholism.

The very early drinking experiences are indicators of later involvement in alcoholism for men. The prevalent gamma type alcoholism has a common denominator in the cultural myth that it is manly to be able to drink a great deal of liquor and hold it. Boys and young men share the misconception that manliness and self-assertion are enhanced by being able to drink.

The male drinker and, to a lesser extent, the female drinker tend to follow sedulously the drinking patterns of those they admire or imitate — the peer figures in their social group. In the alarms and excursions against teenaged drinking which burst forth from time to time in magazines, newspapers, and television, the point is usually missed that teenagers are imitating adult behavior and responding to the stimuli of hard and soft sell advertising in which the act of drinking is always depicted as the preoccupation of youth.

Men who become alcoholics drink in the way they learned to drink as youths. This is true whether you are talking about the son of a minister who preached total abstinence or the son of an alcoholic. The minister's children drink out of curiosity to find out why the substance has been forbidden to them, and the alcoholic's children drink because they have observed how alcohol was used as a problem solver.

As was mentioned before, after World War II when hundreds of thousands of men in their late teens were taken into the armed services, one heard the lament of parents: "They took my boy, a nice innocent kid, and when he came back he was a drunk." In short, military service was blamed for the drinking behavior of the young man. The Veterans Administration, as a matter of policy, rejected alcoholism for a long time as a service connected disability, the reason being that the government undertook no responsibility for the sumptuary regulation of the lives of service personnel insofar as use of liquor is concerned.

As the veterans of World War II approached the age of forty, when alcoholism frequently becomes manifest, a flood of war veterans reached the treatment centers.

The Consultation and Guidance Service of Greater Boston Council on Alcoholism, noting these referrals from industry for treatment in a single age group, devised a simple set of test questions.

"When did you first drink enough to become intoxicated?" and "What was your most memorable drinking experience?"

In a series of thirty World War II veterans the responses to these questions evoke almost identical answers. The first intoxication took place after they had entered the service; most of their drinking before that had been beer or experimentation with very small quantities of hard liquor. In all cases, the most memorable drinking experience had occurred in the service, far away from home, and had ranged from five-day drunks on leave in some foreign place to explosive drinking on pass or liberty in an all-male environment.

This added up to the conclusion that these young men had learned to drink to excess in surroundings where excessive drinking behavior was accepted and admired. The young man whose most cherished memory of a drinking occasion was of staying drunk on "torpedo juice" for several days at Ulithi Atoll or the soldier who saved up beer rations for a fortnight's bustout in Sicily was a prime candidate for alcoholism inasmuch as drinking to excess appeared to him to be normal drinking behavior.

Occupations or professions carry with them cultural vulnerability, which, when aggravated by excessive drinking, is a contributory cause of alcoholism. The traveling salesman who, as part of his selling technique, drinks with customers as well as to pass the time in overnight stops out of town and away from home is much more likely to become an alcoholic than the home-based man who sleeps in his own home every night. Lawyers and doctors, whose professions put demands upon not only their mental alertness but also upon their ability to maintain status in a social drinking society, are more vulnerable to alcoholism than an artisan whose job is skilled but humdrum.

The caretaking professions and occupations yield a sad harvest of alcohol-dependent people because they are required to take on not only their own tensions and anxieties but the tensions and anxieties of others. Thus, the incidence of alcoholism among nurses, clergymen, doctors, and other occupations dealing directly with sick and dependent people is very high, all out of proportion to the knowledge of the danger of utilizing alcohol as a problem solver, tension reliever, or anxiety suppressor.

Many of the rewards that males derive from the use of alcohol are illusory or pure myth. For many, drinking is a ritual, surrounded by a fog of myth.

"A duck can't fly on one wing," is a pure rationalization to account for the second drink. "A touch of whiskey to keep off the chill." The warming effect of whiskey is deceitful. All that has happened is a rush of blood to the surface capillaries making one feel warmer, but in actual practice alcohol provides a quick and easy way to freeze to death on a bitter night because it brings the blood to the skin's surface to be chilled faster.

A drink to "settle" one's stomach is ridiculous. Alcohol as an aperitif works if only a small quantity is used, but too much simply destroys an appetite for food. The alcoholic, on the other hand, who gorges food while drinking in the belief that it prevents intoxication has only postponed the rise in blood-alcohol level and the effect of alcohol as it enters the blood stream.

The rationalizations of alcoholics have a wide range of implausibility and are understood only by therapists in the light of knowledge that alcohol loosens the inhibitions and affects the judgment center of the brain. If we select a common expression of alcohol users and subject it to examination, it will be seen to be ridiculous, and yet it is a rationalization subscribed to by the vast majority of people. They say, "We will wait to have our first drink until the sun goes over the yardarm." They mean that they will not drink alcoholic beverages until after the sun has passed the zenith. Or they will gather together for "sundowners," the drinks before dinner when the sun is going down. The man who downs his drink with the expression, "First today," is calling attention to the fact that he has waited for his first drink in accordance with the rationalization of a drinking society that there is something odd about a person who drinks before these hours. One who drinks in the morning is very definitely branded peculiar and possibly alcoholic. Yet the physiological fact is that the regulation of drinking by the clock is a trait more common to alcoholics than to nonalcoholics. If one is not an alcoholic, the time of day when one elevates the blood-alcohol level by an ounce or two of alcohol has nothing to do with involvement in the disease process, but it has a great deal to do with typical alcoholic behavior.

Many alcoholics shoot for a particular hour when they will have their first drink. Often it is the hour when they are released from employment situations. They can and do adhere to their drinking hours for long periods of time and lose control when some crisis occurs which they believe requires their favorite problem solver. Morning drinking, for example, is not always an indicator that a person is an alcoholic. It is an unusual hour to drink, and those who drink in the morning usually do so because, historically, alcoholics aroused by the pangs of a hangover of massive proportions have always needed liquor to bring their blood-alcohol level up to the point where their psychic and physical pain is bearable. They call it taking "a hair of the dog that bit you."

It has been observed that many male alcoholics have a work pace that is spasmodic. When they are drinking they will pace themselves, avoid making decisions, slow down to a deliberate stroll, find excuses for their altered behavior. But, when they are not drinking, they will tear into their work in a frenzy of activity to make up for lost time, fully aware that they have been procrastinating on the job.

Therapists hear with stupefying frequency the explanation by alcoholics that they drink because they are nervous, and it calms them to have a drink. This is the simple truth which conceals the rationalization, which is, that they are always in a state of nerves, most often because it is the easy explanation of their addiction to liquor. The longer they use liquor as a problem solver the more sensitive their nerves become.

Frequently alcoholics employ the rationalization of denial to allay the concern of someone near and dear to them about their condition. Denial works because few people have the knowledge of alcoholism necessary to call the alcoholic's bluff. Alcoholics taxed with their addiction will almost certainly exclaim, "You are mistaken. Why, I go to work every day. I haven't missed a day in years. I have never even been arrested for drunkenness. Sure, I take a drink, but I can hold it, which is more than some people can say."

The fact is that those working in the field of alcoholism have heard this from alcoholics on the very verge of going into delirium tremens and have had to admit that these rationalizations were true, except that they were meaningless in establishing whether or not the individual was an alcoholic. The alcoholic was playing upon the mass misconceptions of alcoholism and describing a stereotyped derelict, one suffering from a type of alcoholism that afflicts only three percent of all alcoholics.

There are alcoholics who have never been seen drunk, who have never permitted anyone to smell liquor on their breath, and who have successfully evaded recognition of their trouble until they became so deeply involved in the progress of the disease that they were at death's door. A classic example is the expression, "sober as a judge." But who will argue that judges, too, never have trouble with alcohol and become alcoholics, even though one seldom sees them on the bench in a state of intoxication? One can draw some significant conclusions concerning the sobriety of judges from the fact that the legal profession, from which most judges are drawn, has a high rate of alcoholism in our social drinking society, one of the higher rates among professional men.

~~~~~~

CHAPTER 4

INNER RECOGNITION

WHEN THE CASE HISTORIES of alcoholics are studied as a reflection of the drinking practices and drinking behavior of the time in which the alcoholics lived, it seems remarkable that medical historians made so little impression on the general public with their observations of alcoholism as a sickness. But we can clearly see how Americans over a period of three hundred years held to an erroneous concept that those who become drunk in public should be punished and those who keep their drinking behavior private can drink as they please. The consequence has been that there is little or no inner recognition of a drinking problem and no course adopted to remedy it.

Excessive drinking behavior is not new to the United States. Many people will go no farther back than national prohibition when they seek to establish that heavy drinking in mixed company began in that time. Prohibition is simply the event nearest to our own times when drinking behavior and drinking practices underwent social change. Most people disregard the long agitation of the "drys" to curb the use and sale of liquor, a movement that gained strength throughout the latter part of the nineteenth century and culminated in prohibition at the end of World War I. The American people had been conditioned by incessant public agitation to accept a sumptuary law that would curb the use of alcohol as a beverage. The reaction was immediate. It took the form of flouting the law, the rise of a criminal element catering to defiant lawbreakers, and to organized effort to bring about repeal of the prohibition amendment. But national prohibition did not bring about drinking in mixed company or introduce hard drinking to the United States.

Even as there are alcoholics today and even as such people contracted their illness while drinking socially in mixed company, there were alcoholics back in 1620 who contracted their illness while drinking socially in mixed company. They were misunderstood and misrepresented, even as they are today. One might suppose that, in the course of three hundred years of hard drinking, the American people would have acquired the polish of experience and the control of moderation. With the history of the erratic efforts of the American people to control the production, use, and profits of the liquor industry, however, it is not surprising that alcoholism was held to be a crime and not a health problem. No great perceptive talent is needed to understand why people prefer to conceal alcoholism, rather than to expose and treat it.

The users of this chemical, once described as "a domesticated drug to which society has attached certain prestige value," adopted a self-justifying code and a stereotype to distinguish those who are drunkards from those who are social drinkers. Get drunk in public and you must go to jail. Drink as you please in private. They dressed their stereotype of the drunkard in rags, painted his nose red, gave him a mottled complexion and bleary eyes, banished him from respectability, and gave a description of the chronic police-case inebriate or Skid Row drunk as being typical of the alcoholic. In this way, social drinkers could continue to dress the part and act the part of the convivial users of alcohol, secure from disclosure of heavy drinking behavior, even though among them were those similarly dressing and acting the part of social drinkers who were in advanced stages of alcoholism.

One is reminded of the case of William Lloyd Garrison, struggling with Abolitionists to free the slaves, while his brother, addicted to alcohol, was shunted from one concealment to another. Fortunately the alcoholic brother left a record of his struggle with alcohol. One is compelled to wonder what might have happened before the Civil War had William Lloyd Garrison devoted his extraordinary energies to striving to free those other slaves — the alcoholics.

Perhaps the earliest sign of inner recognition of an alcoholism problem experienced by individuals down through the years of our drinking history as Americans is the resentment felt by those who are in trouble with alcohol when their attention is brought to the similarity of their symptoms to those of the Skid Row alcoholic. The most hopeful change in attitude, which may eliminate this resentment and direct the attention of alcoholics to more meaningful signs of alcoholism, is going on today. The findings of the Federal Circuit Courts of Appeal and the U.S. Supreme Court will be discussed in a later chapter. The effect of this change in attitude is that the courts have held that intoxicated alcoholics are sick people, to be treated, not jailed.

One arrives at a better understanding of the status value given by early stage alcoholics to the use of this "domesticated drug" when it is considered that only three to five percent of all alcoholics are chronic police-case inebriates. The majority of early alcoholics use that stigmatized minority to carry the guilt. When alcohol users have had some intimations that they are drinking more than is good for them and creating difficulties for themselves and for others, one can reasonably ask why they do not cut down on their drinking or abstain altogether.

To be reasonable, let us say at the very outset that most steady drinkers are aware, to some extent, that a certain

amount of risk of addiction is attached to drinking. Their
handicap is that their knowledge of the nature of the risk is
sketchy. The average drinker knows that under certain conditions the physical upset caused by drinking too much is
acute and that they have experienced a painful hangover.
They do not know, or do not want to know, that the connection between excessive drinking and alcoholism, or compulsive drinking, is related to their physical condition and their
emotional state. People who drink regularly, every day, even
moderately, may have undergone the transformation from
social drinker to compulsive drinker without knowing that
their psychological makeup and their habituation were favorable to the onset of alcoholism. They do not even want to
know what a compulsion is, yet their habitual use of alcohol
has left them with a physical demand to have a certain amount
of alcohol to maintain a blood-alcohol level which will ease
their discomfort.

If it were possible for the habituated alcoholic to recognize
the compulsiveness and to set up strict controls, alcoholism
would not be a health problem. But it isn't possible to establish strong restrictions for all occasions, because alcoholics do
not recognize compulsiveness until they are "hooked," and
then it is no longer possible to control drinking on all occasions. Even the changes in personality are so subtle and gradual that it is often difficult for the most accurate observers of
alcoholic behavior to recognize any but the most overt examples of changed personality, even in someone they know.

The first ripple of apprehension, the thing the French call
a *frisson,* is meaningful in identification of compulsive drinking. A few case histories of early drinking experiences will
illustrate how nearly normal the continued use of alcohol
appears to be in the individuals beset by alcoholism. Yet the
time came when they experienced that shudder of apprehension, almost a signal, of deep trouble ahead. The following
cases will illustrate these points:

1. Arthur grew up in a small Eastern industrial city in a middle class home. As a boy he was rather awkward and retiring. After being graduated from high school and serving in the Navy, he was employed as a trainee textile supervisor. With adult experience, he gained poise and a dry sense of humor in his communication with other men.

His first taste of liquor was some sherry his father gave him at Thanksgiving dinner. Between high school and his trainee job he spent the years from eighteen to twenty-two in the Navy, and once, while on leave in Newcastle-on-Tyne, he got drunk but was so ill that for months afterwards he couldn't stand the smell of alcohol.

With women he was very shy and almost inarticulate. Girl workers in the textile plant teased him, calling him Silent Art. He began drinking with a group of young men his own age who were also in the training program. Every Saturday night they went to a public dance hall, carrying a couple of pints of liquor. They sneaked drinks when the policemen assigned to keep order at the dance hall were not looking. After a couple of drinks, Arthur found that he was less shy. He could then walk up to a girl and ask her to dance.

It was probably this use of alcohol that endeared it to Arthur. It made him outgoing, and he was able to talk with girls more lightheartedly than he had ever been able to before, when he had made his awkward and frequently tongue-tied efforts to converse with the opposite sex. He had convinced himself that alcohol made others like him and respect him.

By the time Arthur was thirty, married, and the father of two children, he felt he had solved most of the problems he had with interpersonal relations. A few drinks turned him from being a normally taciturn individual into a different person, outgoing, talkative, and likable. He developed in his job and achieved status, but for reasons other than he believed. Arthur thought that he advanced in his work because they liked the Arthur that he was after a drink or two. Actually, he advanced to better positions because he didn't make glaring mistakes, he appeared on the job regularly, he was courteous and considerate, and was a good and useful employee.

His first feeling of apprehension came when his boss, irritated by Arthur's garrulity, said, "Why let booze do all your talking for you? Say nothing and saw wood."

Arthur knew that he had become dependent upon alcohol to prod him into action, but he didn't know of any other way to be acceptable. While he struggled to maintain an outward aspect of a false Arthur, a convivial, jolly, witty fellow, he found that those upon whom he depended were bored with his excessive drinking. He knew of no way, however, to reverse his disastrous course. He continued trying to set up convivial drinking situations, but more and more he was excluded from the group. He was tiresomely concerned with drinking to the exclusion of other recreation. As his long masquerade as a social drinker and good companion approached its end, he felt keen resentment against the group and planned to reject them before they rejected him. He dropped all his old friends and fellow workers. He drank thereafter with strangers or drank alone.

2. Alma, in her early drinking experiences, showed a lack of understanding that what constitutes heavy drinking can be detected. Alma had every reason to believe that she was not a heavy drinker. In fact, most social drinkers would regard her as a light drinker. But Alma became a very sick alcoholic by her thirty-second year.

Alma had quite a normal childhood as far as one can determine from her parents and two brothers. She was the eldest of three children, and both parents were equally fond and proud of her. She was not merely pretty, but very striking. During high school she was very popular. Boys were always around the house. She didn't date a great deal because she was busy with improving herself. She took singing lessons and piano lessons and studied modern dance. She also attended an excellent secretarial school.

She worked only a short time as a secretary because a dance teacher, who had been a dancer in musical comedy, asked her if she would like to try out for the chorus of a new show. She was chosen, and the show settled down for a long run in New York. Her mother lived with her for a time, anxious about Alma's involvement in the theatre, but she soon discovered that the life of a chorus girl is scarcely up to the somewhat garish and sensational pictures of it in the popular press. Alma worked too hard to carry on a hectic high life. Besides, she was seriously studying the dramatic arts.

Alma explained that at this time she was quite lonely and didn't date very much. Eventually, she fell in love with an assistant stage manager, and they were married just before the show went on the road for a national tour. They continued the daily ritual of a couple of drinks after the performance, when they had their largest meal of the day. The marriage lasted two years, and they separated not for lack of compatibility but because they were working in different theatrical productions and were not together enough.

If there was anything permanent about Alma's life at that time it was her daily use of alcohol — not much, remember — two drinks. What she didn't know about her drinking was that she had become dependent on it. Her day was oriented to that hour at night when she would have two stiff highballs, one after the other, and feel her dissatisfaction with herself and her life melt away.

She tried once or twice to forego the liquor, but she stayed wakeful and couldn't sleep. In Alma's case, she had rigid ideas about the propriety of taking more than her quota of two drinks. She knew that she showed her liquor. She had the kind of skin that mottles after a few drinks.

Why did she continue to drink when her mirror warned her of the bad effect liquor had on her appearance? She sat in front of a brightly lighted dressing room mirror at least once a day.

In the first place, Alma was not a vain woman, in itself strange for a woman in the theatre whose looks are a part of her salable product. If Alma had known the truth earlier, she would not have stayed in the theatre because she would have made a very much better secretary than the small bit-playing actress she became. She continued in the theatre because she wanted to please her parents, who liked to refer to her as "our daughter who is on the stage." Her stagestruck mother had made some sacrifices to prepare Alma for the stage, and Alma felt that she owed her parents an effort to pursue a career in the theatre. Besides, she hoped for a reconciliation with her husband.

One day, she experienced as she entered the stage door an overpowering revulsion against the looks, the smell, the sounds, and the frightful tedium of her life backstage. So the time had arrived when Alma's days and nights were oriented to those two drinks she gave herself as a reward for having gotten through another day of a life and an occupation that she hated. She would not drink before a performance, ever, because her performance would be impaired. So she went on — two drinks after the performance, three drinks, four, five, and then drinking to insensibility. She had slipped into alcoholism without ever understanding that, small as her intake had been, she had become dependent upon alcohol, then habituated to alcohol. She hadn't known it until the night she entered the stage door and felt that overpowering revulsion.

3. In Dave's case, one might say the hazards of winter were the cause of his compulsive drinking. Dave was a salesman covering the New England territory by automobile. Fear of mechanical failure of his car and fear of skidding on wet or icy roads became almost an obsession after he had gone unscathed through a skidding accident while speeding to main-

tain a burdensome schedule of sales calls. He went to extraordinary lengths to insure mechanical reliability — a new car every year, extra and excessive checkups of equipment, with always the fear of death in an accident in the back of his mind.

Part of his sales chore was customer relations. Almost every night, in a different town, he entertained customers. The result was jangled nerves and jittery driving and mounting apprehension.

He realized at last that he was drinking too much. The first shudder of comprehension that linked his use of alcohol to his way of life came when he first became certain that he would die of a skidding accident on an icy road. After a trip of one hundred miles or so in winter weather, he would arrive at his destination wringing wet with perspiration. After garaging his car he would need several drinks before he could eat dinner and several more to knock himself out to get some sleep.

When his employers learned of Dave's terror, they urged him to travel by train, bus, or taxi in bad weather. But Dave found that his sales dropped off. He couldn't make as many calls. So he went back to driving himself. He was aware of what this was doing to him, but he couldn't stop. Eventually, fortifying himself with a couple of straight shots of whiskey in preparation for a bad stretch of driving, he had an accident — the one he had long expected — a downhill skid into a culvert. Dave wound up in the hospital with a fractured vertebra, and, after they put him into traction, he immediately went into withdrawal symptoms. Now, at least, he had to face the fact that he was an alcoholic. That is too long a struggle to detail here. If he had heeded his apprehensions and sought psychiatric help, his alcoholism could have been avoided.

4. Karen: Alcohol is such a trickster in the rewards it seems to give to people who are aware that alcohol is causing them deep and prolonged trouble. Most often, by the time the al-

coholic has to make a choice, his ability to choose wisely has been so seriously impaired that nothing can be done without help from others.

Karen didn't discover that there was any difference between her drinking and that of the social group to which she belonged until her husband was transferred across the country to a new job.

You would have to have seen Karen as a bride — twenty-three, radiant, eager to help her husband establish himself in his career — to understand how and why she became an alcoholic. At the time of her marriage there was a great deal of nonsense published in business magazines about the duties of the corporate wife, how she had to reinforce her husband's image in the company, be a perfect hostess, be above reproach, and yet kindle a gleam in the eye of the president and the chairman of the board.

Karen fitted into the corporate cocktail set. She gave splendid parties and imaginative cocktail hours. She attended all the corporate social functions, served as a hostess at conventions, planned hors d'oeuvres for the office Christmas party — the whole bit. The fact is that Karen was never the woman who got plastered at a company party or tried demonstrating the danse du ventre at the company clambake.

She was always very careful to let Smith College show a trifle more than was necessary, but her competition was mainly girls from small co-ed colleges in the middle west, so she got away with it.

Karen could always be counted on to dance with the comptroller and bump cocktail glasses with the comptroller's waspish wife. She drank unobtrusively and always saw to it that everyone got his or her favorite drink — even brandy Alexanders with plenty of cream for the President's wife.

She had a knack of making it important to have a social drink and did it so skillfully that many people who shared a cocktail with her thought it was their idea. Her intake of alcohol even escaped the notice of her husband — when she made a point of assuring him that her social activities were all channeled into making him a big wheel in the company. A sample of her technique:

"Oh, hello, dear. I'm so glad you made it home for dinner. I had a ghastly afternoon at that bridge. I just had to lose to Mrs. Hillcress. You know how vicious she can be when she loses. We stopped on the way home and I bought her a cocktail at the Surrey. Oh, by the way, your martini is ready — six to one vodka, right? Hurry, take your shower, and I'll leave it on the dresser in the bedroom."

Each small success he had on his job was celebrated with cocktails and dinner at some nice place. Her husband felt that he had acquired a treasure, a mate to reinforce his efforts, mother his children, and ornament his social corporate life with polished perfection.

When his big chance came, that of becoming an executive vice president of a competing company located all the way across the continent, Karen made some slight objections. She would have to find new schools for the children. She didn't know much about the city in which they would live. What about all their furniture? It probably wouldn't be suitable for the West Coast. Through a series of farewell parties she was bright, gay, and seemingly happy, but she had a first dark feeling of foreboding. Her social drinking group, whose needs dovetailed so perfectly with her needs, would be lost.

On the West Coast she tried mightily to re-create another corporate social drinking set, but she was playing in a different league. Now she was the wife of the executive vice president, and executive vice presidents' wives, according to the rules of the corporate wife game, are supposed to remain slightly aloof. You can't organize successful drinking parties, however, and remain aloof. Also, she had moved from an indoor recreation group to an outdoor recreation group into which her kind of party didn't fit.

The day after she shipped her children off to their old schools back East, she found herself drinking alone for the first time — in a quiet house in which, when the telephone rang, it was certain to be her husband saying that he was staying late at the office.

Thirty-six years old, still good looking and well groomed, Karen felt the first ripple of apprehension that the French call a "frisson." She knew she was hooked. Without alcohol she fell apart.

5. Charley and Hattie experienced their forerunning symptoms of alcoholism together. They were married. Charley was a hotel clerk, working from noon to midnight, and Hattie was the cashier in a movie theatre, working from noon to ten-thirty at night. They didn't have any children, and Hattie said afterwards that it was fortunate they didn't.

When they were first married their working hours didn't coincide. Within two years, when it seemed to them that one was always sleeping while the other was wide awake, they quarreled constantly. Hattie finally gave up her bookkeeper's job, day work in an insurance agency, and took the movie cashier job so she would spend more time with Charley. They slept late most mornings and, when they got up, had to dash to work. This got to be rather difficult because they stayed up late, having some social life together.

When Hattie finished work at the box office, turning in her cash at about 10:30 P.M., she would change her makeup, stroll to the downtown hotel where Charley worked, and would wait in the lobby until he was through.

Then they would walk to a nearby cafe, where there was a three-piece combo for dancing, and have a few drinks and some food. Many of the patrons at the cafe also had night jobs and they formed a sort of group, sitting with or near one another, and having a few liberties that were accorded to regular patrons. They could run a bar tab. They were poured bigger drinks than the casual customers. The combo played music for them that they liked. Even when the place was sold and new management took over, the regulars were accorded special attention.

If you asked Charley and Hattie how many drinks they had each night they wouldn't be able to tell you because they didn't keep count. Five or six was about the correct number, however.

Sometimes, instead of walking the ten blocks to their apartment, they would take a cab, and it was always a driver who knew them, one of the regulars on the owl stand next to the cafe. "That joint would go bankrupt without you two," one of the cabbies often said.

"Oh," said Charley, "we don't spend much. We have to eat when we get through work. It's our only meal together all day."

Sometimes, when they awakened late in the morning, both Charley and Hattie would be hung over. It happened once or twice a month. At first Hattie passed the aspirin, but it got so it didn't work so well, even when it was followed by tomato juice and a dash of Worcestershire sauce. Someone told Charley that beer with a raw egg in it was a sure cure, and they tried that. They also tried flat Guinness stout, and they finally settled for a hair of the dog — a stiff shot of bourbon.

"Nothing like it," said Charley. "A hair of the dog — wait half an hour and then a good breakfast."

The trouble was that they didn't always have time for a good breakfast. Charley began having a nip in midafternoon, covered with breath purifiers. Hattie also had a stiff one on her relief in the box office, and she made it vodka, because a bartender told her you couldn't smell vodka on the breath.

It took three years, but Charley and Hattie began to yearn for that witching hour of midnight. Hattie had a solution for the urgency she felt. She arranged to wait for Charley in the cafe and have a quick one while waiting. When Charley came, he had to have two quick ones to catch up with Hattie.

It was their regular cabbie who broke the news to them. "It's none of my business," he said one night as he helped Charley support Hattie to the door of their apartment, "but you two can't knock that stuff around that way, not without it giving you some trouble."

"What kind of trouble?" asked Charley.

"Well, it's your affair."

"What kind of trouble?" Charley insisted.

"Why do you think I'm pushing a cab at my age? I used to own a fleet of cabs. I hit the booze, and now I'm a cabbie again. But, I beat the booze. I'm in AA."

"What's with AA?"

"Alcoholics Anonymous."

"You think we are alcoholics?"

"Charley, just as a friend, I think you'll do until a better model comes along."

Charley and Hattie couldn't remember when they first began to yearn for the ritual in the cafe, but later, when they began telling their drunk story at AA meetings, they agreed that it was the night the cab driver noticed how much time and money they spent in the cafe after work.

Hattie, who has a memory like an elephant, explains: "We never took his cab again. I guess that means something."

These cases illustrate how little of American drinking experience of the past 350 years has carried over into a cultural defense against improper use of alcoholic beverages. If this lack of defense against an excessive drinking culture were limited to the case histories presented here, there would be no concern about alcoholism. Those who read the case histories carefully, however, will detect in them bits of problems with drinking that they or their friends have experienced and, if they will reflect, will understand that compulsive drinking can appear to be so normal.

CHAPTER **5**

~~~~~~

MOTIVATION FOR TREATMENT

AT THIS POINT in development of our social drinking society, it is not particularly helpful to debate the meaning of the terms excessive drinking, heavy drinking, compulsive drinking, dependent drinking, and other generalizations, because what is intolerable drinking to one individual may very well be tolerable to another. It should be left to the individuals to define these terms for themselves on the basis of factual information material developed from scientific sources.

If there were standards by which excess could be measured in terms of the number of drinks ingested, it might be possible to declare, as several investigators have, that "safe" drinking is possible if one arrives late at cocktail parties, takes only one weak drink or none at all, and in any case limits drinks to two a day and considers that five drinks on a weekend is "heavy drinking." The fact is that many social drinkers may have as many as five drinks at social events a couple of times a week and still not be regarded in their group as heavy drinkers. Or, as an old AA joke puts it, some drinkers may spill more than that in a week, and still not be considered heavy drinkers by their group. Manifestly, there is no safe way for an alcoholic to drink, because the alcoholic is a compulsive drinker and has no means of controlling intake, once he has started drinking.

As we get into the question of motivating a person to undergo treatment, one must know what kind of social group the individual belongs to, how that group drinks, and their attitude towards alcoholism, before it can be determined whether the individual and the group are excessive, moderate, or compulsive. Each social drinking group offers an alcoholic considerable concealment until overt alcoholic behavior arouses the social group to action. Such action may be exclusion from the group by either expressed or implied disapproval. The group's feeling is that the alcoholic member has attracted unfavorable notice to the group's drinking behavior, and so, if they want to continue to drink socially, the alcoholic must not be allowed to use the group for concealment. In effect, those in the group express a collective moral judgment exculpating themselves from responsibility in the matter.

The alcoholic individual can place no reliance on what his social group will do and even less on what he can do for himself. Alcoholics have an inner recognition that they drink in a manner much different from others in the group who are not compulsive. Suppose the group customarily has two or three cocktails each on a social drinking occasion. The alcoholic manages to have many more. The alcoholic cannot overlook this discrepancy in behavior. This is the first point of inner recognition of a drinking problem.

Another notable difference in a social drinking group is that the alcoholic member will usually be first to suggest having a drink, is usually an eager volunteer bartender, and is quick to call upon others to drink up and have another. This preoccupation with drinking is expressed in many ways. Some carry a drink to the table from the cocktail hour; some are adept at slipping to the source of liquor for a quick drink; some arrive with a head start; seldom do they leave an unfinished drink.

After a time — and a longer time than one might imagine — the group notices the alcoholic's preoccupation with drinking. Then the group will remark out of earshot of the alcoholic that he is drinking too much or will take evasive action to avoid the alcoholic's company.

Having called attention to his preoccupation with drinking, the alcoholic underscores the problem by intoxicated behavior, sometimes raucous, frequently noisy and clownish, and often lacking in dignity or aplomb. Little more proof of alcoholism is needed than the ingenious and imaginative explanations the alcoholic volunteers to account for drunken behavior. The alibi is the alcoholic's main reliance to prevent rejection by his social group. If they accept his lighthearted alibis, he has gained their further indulgence. Because alcoholism is stigmatized, most social arbiters hesitate to speak the nasty word. The alcoholic, however, knows that these are the people who are a threat to his continued drinking.

"They" become the symbol of all those who pose a threat to his need for alcohol. "They" cannot hold their liquor as he does. "They" are not manly or sophisticated. "They" are not sexy or witty or "with it." As the group becomes more critical of the alcoholic, he becomes more critical of them. When the group or some member of it quotes something the alcoholic has said which the alcoholic doesn't remember, they are trying to put something over on him. He doesn't recognize alcoholic amnesia. All he knows is that he pulled a blank, if what they quote is true. Instead of being alarmed, he feels proud that, instead of passing out cold, he continued to function as if he had had only a couple of drinks.

Nevertheless the alcoholic is uneasy about the way he drinks. He knows he drinks differently than the others. They may nurse their drinks. He doesn't fool around with small talk between sips. He knocks them down in a couple of gulps and is ready for more. Nursing a drink is all right if you have had too many, but what he needs is a running start to get to the point of too many.

The running start involves a certain preparation for a drinking occasion. Instead of waiting around for drinks to be served, the alcoholic has a couple before joining the drinking group. If he arrives a trifle tipsy and word gets around that he got plastered before coming to the party, it is time to go into evasive action. That means sneaking drinks.

Careful planning is necessary to sneak drinks while under group observation. If in a public place, he can take a trip to the lavatory with a stop at the bar for a double or a visit to the checkroom for the pint in the topcoat pocket. Then, at private parties, one can always volunteer to be bartender. One for me, one for the guests, and make mine a double.

There is enough difference in the group's drinking behavior and the alcoholic's drinking behavior to make the alcoholic aware that the social drinkers are getting something out of it that he misses. They like the temporary feeling of well-being, the lowering of inhibitions, the camaraderie of a shared drinking experience, but it isn't essential to them. They can be likable, communicative, and interesting without alcohol. The alcoholic needs alcohol for something beyond mere euphoria. Less and less does he need the social mingling that they desire.

What has happened is that the need for alcohol is such that the need isolates him. To him it is irksome to maintain the kind of social interchange that goes with unhindered and unobserved access to enough liquor to satisfy. Whether he drinks at home or in company, his drinking is challenged, threatened, made difficult.

The alcoholic's life arranges itself to link one drinking occasion to the next. If he is a white-collar worker, he has the problem of getting a drink at noon and also of drinking after work with colleagues, while concealing his habituation to alcohol. If he is a blue-collar worker, the main effort is aimed at quitting time or coffee breaks. Both white- and blue-collar workers must find comfort — and remember that they are only really comfortable when drinking.

At some point in alcoholic progression, every alcoholic experiments as a mixologist, switching around from one liquor to another, drinking beer or wine, eliminating soda from highballs, testing strange combinations of chasers and eyeopeners in the hope of finding the combination of potables which will give him the maximum comfort with the minimum aftereffect. Such efforts to manage drinking indicates a concealed inner knowledge that he is drinking because he has to, not because he wants to.

Sometimes so-called geographical escape is attempted in the hope of leaving alcoholic misuse behind and starting anew. Alcoholics will sometimes change residence, change jobs, seek new social groups, change drinking companions. But, no matter what they do, short of getting treatment for their sickness, alcoholism flickers along with them, a silent shadow growing bigger and bigger.

The alcoholic's use of alcohol, once limited to formal social drinking, now has altered and focused on new and strange drinking behavior. Luncheon is a time of day to get enough alcohol to carry through the afternoon. Quitting time means a beginning of serious, purposeful alcoholic drinking. Drinking now has become more important than any other activity. The alcoholic strives to find a drink, a drinking pattern, and drinking companions to fit into his framework of compulsive drinking behavior.

Lone drinking often is the result of failure to discover a milieu in which alcoholic behavior will not be critically observed. The alcoholic refuses to face up to the fact that society is rejecting his drinking behavior when it rejects him as a person. The social drinking code that once included him in a group has closed the door on him. Resentment at his exclusion and refusal to talk about alcoholism drives the alcoholic into isolation or into immature efforts to conceal drinking by the use of breath fresheners and pitiful alibis.

What cannot be concealed, however, is the change of personality. The sweetly reasonable person when sober may become furiously hostile when drinking. The taciturn grouch may become unnaturally happy. There are many psychological explanations for this changed personality, but one of the most important results is self-disgust. To conceal alcoholic behavior, the drinker creates an alibi system which he knows is false and which disgusts him with his dependence on alcohol. The individual who started out drinking as a likable, outgoing, socially adjusted person has become a quarrelsome, self-centered, appallingly selfish, undependable, false friend.

The true test for an alcoholic, skeptical of the expert knowledge of one who is trying to help, is a drinking test. If the alcoholic will state what he believes to be a reasonable intake of alcohol every day, it will probably be something like five highballs a day — stiff ones. Now, if he will agree to stick to five stiff highballs a day for a month, never drinking more than five, never taking less, it will be less than two weeks before the alcoholic loses control, because he has lost the power to control drinking to a regular intake. It is all or nothing with the alcoholic. Many alcoholics, for example, can go on the wagon and stay sober for long periods of time and then, faced with a crisis of one kind or another, they take a drink or two, gradually increasing their intake until they are out of control again.

Even the chronic alcoholic, whose terminations of drinking episodes are fearful experiences — shakes, hallucinations, convulsions — doesn't gain insight alone and unaided because of the pain. He will repeat again and again, unless he regains sobriety and maintains it for the rest of his life, advocates of the controlled drinking of recovered alcoholics notwithstanding.

What may seem to the alcoholic to be controlled drinking may get out of hand in the most subtle and deceptive ways. In the first place, the alcoholic who believes his drinking is controlled is unable to measure the gradual rise of the blood-alcohol level. The vulnerability to alcohol lurking in the adaptive cells of the alcoholic's body does not, as some believe, instantaneously trigger a drinking episode. Some personal crisis — the death of a relative, the loss of a job, a social rebuff, a deep frustration — calls for euphoria of the kind provided by alcohol. In very short order there is established as firmly as ever the old pattern of drinking for relief, drinking out of control, drinking in defiance of the conventions of one's group.

The writer has known only two individuals who were even moderately successful in resuming drinking after acute bouts with alcoholism. One died of a coronary thrombosis within five months after resuming moderate use of alcohol. No one, not even the pathologist, could determine whether alcohol was the cause of the heart attack or whether it would have been possible for him to continue moderate use of alcohol after recovery from the coronary thrombosis. The other individual found after a year of moderate drinking that the pressures and uncertainty aroused by the necessity of being constantly on guard against relapse were too great to be borne. He quit for good.

Every alcoholic is familiar with the technique of nipping. It means just a little bit of alcohol, which, deceptively, seems to do him no harm. The quantity ingested becomes larger and larger until once again he is out of control. The only difference is postponement of the time when his blood-alcohol level will have built up to a point high enough to trigger an all-out relapse.

Our American drinking culture is a hostile environment for alcoholics, because everyone who uses alcoholic beverages — even most moderate social drinkers — feels a certain amount of residual guilt about drinking. The new freedom of the sexes mingling in heavy drinking situations is not really a new freedom, but behavior that has existed for 350 years in this country emerging into the open. Psychological clues to this residual guilt about drinking linger in the shuttered and curtained bars and taverns, the dimly lit cocktail lounges, the subtle concealment of drinking occasions. Away down deep is buried a feeling of guilt. A great deal of hypocrisy may be found in the drinking manners and mores of Americans. The Frenchman who stops in for a drink on his way to work does so without any feeling of guilt. But the American seen in a bar at eight in the morning isn't exactly elated at being discovered drinking in the morning.

People are even more guilt ridden when they drink alone. It amounts to a confession that one's drinking is abnormal. Many a drunken husband or drunken wife is hidden by the family because they are ashamed and share guilt for this abnormal drinking behavior. Society is caught in a web of drinking guilts, and these guilts tend to be more destructive of alcoholics and their families. The families of drunken neighbors suffer cruel ostracism by the social group to which they belong, whatever their level of income or society.

Treatment of alcoholics would be very much easier and far more effective if alcoholics, recognizing that their drinking behavior is different from that of nonalcoholic family members, friends, and neighbors, would seek qualified expert counseling. It is not possible today to encounter uniform attitudes of goodwill towards alcoholics in need of treatment, whether it be from family, employers, friends, or physicians who are consulted or involved with an alcoholic person.

Wives, parents, children, and close friends of alcoholics generally attempt at first to excuse or explain away an alcoholic's drinking behavior. As failure and frustration diminish their hopes for a "cure," those closest to an alcoholic will go to the other extreme and attempt to saddle the alcoholic with all the guilt and blame. The alcoholic is gradually phased out of all that the family living room implies, into all that the back bedroom implies. His function in the family is taken over. Most often the alcoholic lives under the supervision of former loved ones, who have become policemen and detectives toward him. Even worse, the family members may have taken over the doctor's function, simply because they have been unable to establish contact with a doctor trained to treat alcoholics.

The American Medical Association (AMA) is now in the midst of an educational effort to familiarize doctors with alcoholism and its treatment. But the AMA is aware of the monumental scope of the problem. All too many doctors will slap an alcoholic on the back or, if the patient is a woman, pat a hand and say, "You are not an alcoholic. You have just got to cut down on your drinking." Far too often the patient given this advice is an alcoholic, and the last thing he is capable of is cutting down on his drinking.

Families threatened by alcoholic disruption can take constructive steps to help the alcoholic member. A few are listed below:

1. Recognize that alcoholism isn't hopeless and that it is a treatable disease.

2. Consult a reliable source about what steps to take. If a family doctor gives that "just-cut-down-on-drinking" prescription, try the clergyman. If the clergyman cannot refer you to a resource or give counseling himself, look up your alcoholism information center in the telephone book and make an appointment. As an alternative, look up Al-Anon Family Groups or Alcoholics Anonymous in the telephone book, then ask them for the name and address of a reliable counselor.

3. Do not attempt to hide the alcoholic or shield him from the consequences of compulsive drinking.

4. Stop condemning liquor, drinking, and drinking companions because you will only stir up resentment.

5. Do not make a neighborhood discussion project of the family's alcoholic member. Talk about the problem only with those who can give constructive help.

6. Make your home life and family activities as normal as possible and always remember you have a sick person in the house.

7. Stop nagging.

8. If you have to take over the alcoholic's family responsibilities, do it without making a Federal case of it and be prepared, as the alcoholic recovers, to give those responsibilities back to him.

9. Try to think about the alcoholic's plight in terms of what is good for him, not what is bad for you.

10. Alcoholics have their good points. Stress them and reinforce them.

11. Stop hunting down hidden liquor and by all means do not pour out what you find. The first priority in an alcoholic's life is a supply of liquor. He will replace the supply you pour out.

12. Once you have received competent advice, follow it. Do not try to be a therapist. You are too close to the problem and too emotionally involved to always be objective.

If the foregoing suggestions are followed, families will be playing an important role in pretreatment motivation of the alcoholic. Successful motivation prevents time wasting in treatment. Instead of costly shopping around to find a therapy acceptable to the alcoholic, families find that their alcoholic member is preconditioned to accept treatment. Motivation requires skillful timing and good judgment. The therapists, who are in short supply, possess a knowledge of the reasoning of alcoholics, particularly with reference to when and how they will accept and cooperate with treatment techniques. Such motivation requires more or less a free hand and discriminatory judgment not only in dealing with the alcoholic but also in dealing with the families, the employers, and others directly affected by the alcoholic's sickness.

Some alcoholics will attempt to give lip service to the suggestions of the therapists with a view to continuing to drink.

Therapists are skilled in circumventing these schemes of alcoholics because they are experienced in such behavior on the part of sick people.

Families of alcoholics should be encouraged by the demonstrable scientific fact that alcoholics from time to time recognize that they drink differently than others — too often, too fast, and too much. That time usually coincides with a psychological slump — a kind of despair more simply described as "hitting bottom." A great deal of judgment must be exercised by therapists in persuading families to keep hands off, as well as in persuading alcoholics to heed the warning of this alcoholic crisis.

A genuine case history may illustrate how pretreatment motivation operates. Many, many alcoholics coast past the crisis, when they really hit bottom, through the protective actions of family members. Often it would have been better for the crisis to occur, rather than have the family postpone it.

Joel was a husband and father in his forties. In his excessive drinking he ran very serious risks, because he had what amounted to an obsession about his ability to drive an automobile. He would brag that he had been driving a car since he was fourteen and that his reflexes were such that an automobile became practically an extension of his own being.

As a successful accountant, Joel was regarded as an enthusiastic social drinker, but his wife knew that he was an alcoholic. Her greatest fear was that he would have a serious accident while driving and that it would have a serious effect on his business if it got into the small town newspaper in their home community. She went to extraordinary lengths to take his automobile keys away from him when he was drinking, but she feared she wouldn't always be able to prevent him from using one of the family cars.

When she confided these fears to a therapist she was advised to stop agonizing over the possibility of her husband's driving while intoxicated because it was causing her a severe neurosis. She was simply to inform her husband that if he attempted to drive while drinking she would report him to the police.

"Oh, you won't do that," Joel said when his wife told him of her intentions.

Joel had his drunken driving accident soon after that. He ran into a stone wall, smashed up his car, fractured his nose, cut his face on his broken eyeglasses, and, as a climax, was picked up by police on a drunken driving charge.

The story of his accident and arrest got into the suburban newspaper, and a few clients did cancel their business. But Joel couldn't be sure whether his wife had reported him to the police or whether they had simply responded to an accident call.

"He hasn't been to the office since it happened," Joel's wife reported to the therapist. "He won't leave the house. I believe he thinks I reported him to the police, but he won't say anything or ask me anything."

"Let him think you did report him," said the therapist. And it worked perfectly. Joel's wife remained silent and noncommittal, and Joel believed that she had turned him in to the police. This was for him a psychological low. He had always believed that she would protect him. Now, he feared that he was losing her.

"What can I do to make it up to you?" Joel asked at length.

"You can go see someone I have talked to, who can help you stop drinking," she responded.

Coached by the therapist, Joel's wife continued to show lack of concern about what happened to Joel as long as he continued to drink. She was polite, considerate, and affectionate, but she no longer agonized over Joel's drinking. Finally Joel reported his wife's attitude to the therapist, complaining that if she wouldn't help him, someone had to give him help.

The therapist then described the symptoms of progressive

alcoholism, and Joel recognized some of the things as having happened to him. Joel then said that he had been having a "little" trouble with liquor, that his difficulties at home had always seemed to be connected with drinking, and that his business had suffered since he had been arrested for driving while drunk. He said that he didn't believe he was an alcoholic, but he would cooperate in treatment.

"You are the one to decide whether you are an alcoholic or not," said the therapist. "Shall we start tomorrow with a general physical examination?"

The main effort in pretreatment motivation is to inform families and employers what is going on, what to expect, and to advise them to intervene only under prompting of the therapist. Next comes the effort to be on hand when a crisis occurs or even to create a crisis.

It often happens that a wife will threaten divorce or separation unless the alcoholic spouse mends his ways. After five or six threats of this kind and no action, the alcoholic concludes that it is just an idle threat. Similarly, alcoholic wives dismiss the threats of husbands to take the children away from them, but, in both cases, carrying out the threat of separation or divorce precipitates a crisis often used by therapists as motivation for treatment.

Therapists often consult marriage counselors, lawyers, and sociologists about the advisability of creating a crisis by having the aggrieved spouse carry out the threat of separation or divorce, always leaving the door slightly ajar to restore the marriage if a real effort is made to stop drinking and remain abstinent.

The point is made not to continue to threaten, but to act, to carry out the threat if the alcoholic does not comply with reasonable requests for an effort to change behavior. Some means of compulsion is always useful to the therapist, for the therapeutic effect of a crisis is important in treatment.

Employers, for example, have learned that offering an alcoholic employee an alternative to being fired for drinking is much better motivation than firing the individual immediately. What is done by most employers who today have alcoholism treatment policies is to place the employee on ninety days of probation, giving him an opportunity to dry out and get some treatment. If the individual cooperates in treatment, even though one or two relapses occur, the employee is kept on the job. But the fact is that loss of the job hangs over the alcoholic's head, and it is believed to account for the high rate of recoveries in industrial alcoholism treatment programs. A job has a great deal of importance in the life of an individual.

Pretreatment motivation finds reinforcement also from the nonjudgmental nurses who care for a patient undergoing withdrawal symptoms. The attitude of the nurse, who gives the alcoholic bed care of the same quality as she gives to other sick people, is very meaningful to an alcoholic. The person emerging from the physical and psychic crises of withdrawal is a good subject for pretreatment motivation. Alcoholics are generally willing to swear off when they are in the convalescent stage of recovery from withdrawal symptoms. It is merely a matter of reinforcing those good intentions and not permitting time to elapse between the statement of the good intentions and the actual contact with a therapist who has then the best chance to establish rapport with the alcoholic.

Types of crises meaningful to alcoholics in accepting treatment are too numerous to list, but, in general, any life crisis, any physical crisis, any psychological crisis can be exploited by skilled therapists. They must, however, have a free hand and an understanding with families that there will be no interference, no judgmental pressure outside of treatment.

Often a complete switch in the reaction of spouses, or other close relatives, to the drinking capers of an alcoholic will so baffle alcoholics that they will accept treatment, if only to satisfy their curiosity about what has wrought the change in family attitudes.

It is even possible under skillful management to utilize the long-suffering attitude of a wife who enjoys playing the martyr to motivate an alcoholic to cooperate in treatment. The wife who snatches off her halo and exhibits signs that she doesn't care whether her alcoholic husband is shot off towards the moon in a rocket, as long as she isn't affected, may be crisis enough for an alcoholic to investigate what has happened to his once noble spouse.

The numerous case histories of alcoholism, involving either husband or wife, in which the nonalcoholic partner undertakes to ward off the adverse effects of alcoholism show a surprisingly high percentage of failure. The alcoholic partner can only profit from the abrasive experiences of alcoholic mishaps. Many therapists feel that the alcoholic must suffer the consequence of alcoholic misadventures and that, as is the case with so many doting relatives, efforts to protect the alcoholic from the consequences only postpone the crisis which can be used to therapeutic advantage. The rule of thumb is to let the alcoholic get into trouble and leave the management of this crisis to the therapists.

Whatever course is selected by therapists, a real need is for instruction of the family on the subject of alcoholism, and the teaching of Tender Loving Care in so far as alcoholism is concerned is sometimes as painful to families as the rejection and exclusion they have experienced from the behavior of the alcoholic.

Pretreatment motivation is application of good common sense without sentiment or emotion.

~~~~~~

CHAPTER 6

EFFECTS OF PUBLIC ATTITUDES

PUBLIC AWAKENING to the true nature of alcoholism and acceptance of the fact that it is a treatable disease have made substantial headway during the past few years, particularly in the area of overcoming inertia due to stigma.

From many parts of the United States come reports of aroused communities, shocked by the neglect or mistreatment of alcoholics in need of medical treatment. This concern has not yet clarified the distinction between the problem of the minority of alcoholics, represented by Skid Row or chronic police-case inebriates, and the majority (about eighty to ninety percent), represented by alcoholics who hold jobs, maintain homes, have family relationships, maintain status in their social groups, even if afflicted by alcoholism. While economically the majority enjoy a far better prognosis than the minority, most of the public money spent on alcoholism treatment goes into programs aimed at assisting chronic police-case inebriates and indigent alcoholics, rather than into tackling the majority's problems.

Since 1956 the American Medical Association has held that alcoholism is a treatable disease, even though it cannot be cured. For an even longer time, the voluntary groups working on problems of alcoholism have pleaded for recognition of the treatability of alcoholism. Indeed, even before the AMA declaration of policy, industrial medical facilities had persuaded several large employers to establish policies and treatment programs for alcoholic employees.

Today there is a binding legal determination of the distinction between simple intoxication and alcoholism. Beginning in 1966, with the two landmark decisions by the Fourth Circuit Court of Appeals in the Driver case and the decision of the Washington, D.C., Circuit Court of Appeals in the case of De Witt Easter, it was determined that the alcoholic chronic police-case inebriate is a sick person and that it is cruel and unusual punishment (under the Eighth Amendment to the Constitution) to jail a person whose only offense is illness. The Easter decision had immense impact because of the fact that the court, sitting en banc, handed down its first unanimous decision in a decade.

These two circuit court decisions had the effect of putting into question in every part of the nation the police court practices, the correctional system practices, and the practices of other public custodial care resources regarding chronic police-case inebriates. An enormous revision of popular attitudes towards alcoholics and alcoholism resulted from the admission of a constitutional question concerning a Texas chronic police-case inebriate in the 1968 session of the U.S. Supreme Court. However, while finding alcoholism a treatable disease, the Court decided in favor of Texas, calling its action the only one possible due to disagreement of the disciplines concerned and a present inability to substitute treatment for penal facilities.

These legal decisions had already spurred city, county, and state authorities to seek means of handling the chronic police-case inebriate problems in detoxification centers, treatment resources, and halfway houses. There was also a long-expected effort to find a quick means of transformation from punitive, custodial care, by renaming drunk jails and houses

of correction as medical facilities. But, again, the attempt to
do this in the District of Columbia had foredoomed such
oversimplification of the problem. The American people at
long last had to face the fact that alcoholism is a destructive
illness affecting from 6,500,000 to 15,000,000 dependent or
habituated alcoholics and that it is a public health problem
of comparable magnitude to heart, cancer, or mental illness.

It is still not clearly proven from a scientific standpoint
that the alcoholism experienced by homeless Skid Row alcoholics is the same disease as that suffered by the majority of
alcoholics. It is clear that most alcoholics have a better prognosis for recovery than the Skid Row alcoholic under conditions that have prevailed up to the recent historic court
decisions on alcoholism. If it is the identical disease, then the
future holds the promise of preventive measures which could
eliminate Skid Row alcoholism as well.

There are other reforms concurrent with the legal affirma-
tions. *The Journal of the American Medical Association* for
August 1966 hailed not only the court decisions, but accepted
responsibility for failure to treat alcoholics, particularly the
chronic police-case inebriates. The editorial in its entirety
sets forth the view far more concisely than any abridgement
could:

> Change comes about in strange ways, but at last a change
> in attitude toward the alcoholic patient is being accomplished.
>
> For too many years the plight of alcoholic persons, espe-
> cially those who inhabit skid rows and "drunk tanks" has
> provided the occasion for amusement, disdain, and disap-
> proval. Because of the seemingly insurmountable social and
> administrative barriers, the medical profession has not af-
> forded alcoholics the treatment usually offered to sufferers
> of more clearly defined medical disorders. The jail, with the
> policeman, the judge and probation officer acting as unwill-
> ing accomplices, was made the dumping ground for this
> human "refuse"; here little but futile ritual was exercised,
> and constructive action was seldom undertaken.

Recent application of the 8th Amendment to the United States Constitution confronts us with the fact that alcoholism is an illness and must be treated as such. Our society can no longer ignore the fact that it is wrong to punish another human being for being sick, even if the sickness is alcoholism.

The decisions in the Driver case in the Fourth Circuit Court in North Carolina and the Easter case in the Circuit Court for the District of Columbia are important landmarks. In each decision alcoholism not only received legal recognition as a disease, but frequent appearance in public in an intoxicated state is defined as a symptom of alcoholism, not a criminal offense. Judge Bryan said of the alcoholic in the North Carolina decision "this addiction — chronic alcoholism — is now almost universally accepted medically as a disease. The symptoms, as already noted, may appear as a 'disorder of behavior.' Obviously this includes appearances in public, as here, unwilled and ungovernable by the victim. When that is conduct for which he is criminally accused, there can be no judgment of criminal conviction passed upon him. To do so would affront the 8th Amendment as cruel and unusual punishment in branding him a criminal, irrespective of consequent detention and fine."

These decisions do not negate statutes punishing ordinary public drunkenness; neither do they deal with the issue of the culpability of persons carrying out unlawful and antisocial acts while under the influence of alcohol. They do portend, however, the end to the time-worn practice of meeting the problems of public drunkenness on the part of chronic alcoholic persons primarily by incarcerating them as criminals. This change in attitude also presents to the medical profession and others a forceful challenge to create nationwide programs for those afflicted with problems with alcohol.

Our most immediate task is the development of specific guidelines for the diagnosis of alcoholism, which are as clear and precise as possible, and which satisfy both medical and legal definitions. A second obligation will be to foster the admission of alcoholics to those general hospitals that do not now admit such patients and to help establish detoxification units which can function in close affiliation with long-term treatment centers and associated agencies. We must assure that provisions for treatment are medically sound and that all paramedical personnel are under the supervisory responsibility of physicians. Next, we should play an important role not only in the education of many members of our own profession but also in educating police and other concerned groups about issues of acute and chronic alcoholic infirmities. Finally, we must integrate as coequals or as consultants our specialized skills with those of all other professions which have been involved traditionally in the management of alcoholic persons, in those long-term endeavors in which purely psychiatric or other medical factors are not predominant.

The Driver and Easter decisions represent a legal extension of the position adopted by the American Medical Association in 1956 and reaffirmed in its 1962 statement on the hospitalization of alcoholics. They indicate that the medical profession soon will face increasing responsibility for a wide range of manifestations of alcoholic problems previously left primarily to law enforcement agencies. The extent to which we assist the alcoholic person in obtaining proper medical and other meaningful help will be a measure of our response to the challenge implicit in these decisions.

This statement has been approved for publication by the members of the Committee on Alcoholism and Addiction and the Council on Mental Health.

Clarification of the legal status of alcoholism will place a temporary strain on available treatment resources, including the scarce detoxification units now so ardently advocated for chronic police-case inebriates. The problem of scarcity will be better understood if one considers that treatment of alcoholism is divided into three main segments — the well-to-do, who can afford expensive treatment which now exists in plush mental health centers, sanatoria, and private alcoholism hospitals; the middle income group, who can afford only moderate outlay for treatment of alcoholism, treatment which is almost completely lacking in every American community; and treatment for the chronic police-case inebriates, whose care and custody now consumes large amounts of public funds with minimal results.

Detoxification centers are intended mainly for the latter, although the middle income group could benefit from detoxification centers operated in conjunction with general hospital treatment resources. A detoxification center does not treat alcoholism per se. It merely provides a noncondemning resource where the alcoholic can be sobered up and motivated to accept treatment. This means short-term bed care, diagnosis, and referral to long-term treatment as an outpatient.

The new legal concept is that the custodial care given to police-case inebriates under court order bears the stigma of a criminal record and that the law errs in punishing one whose situation is due to disease or illness. The problem can be aggravated by the confusion and strain in treatment resources now available if the entire problem of detoxifying and treating the chronic inebriate segment is dumped on the very limited facilities. Even now, with many police court judges questioning their right to commit alcoholics to jail, the strain is showing, and neither state nor federal governments have appropriated money to provide enough detoxification and treatment units.

One of the bright hopes for reinforcing treatment programs has been provided by industrial medicine. Many of the modern techniques for outpatient treatment of alcoholism have been pioneered by industrial medical men in response to the need of industry to conserve and rehabilitate employees suffering from alcoholism. At the outset industrial medicine and industry leadership called such on-the-job techniques of handling alcoholic employees a humanitarian gesture. The plain fact, now generally accepted by enlightened employers, is that it costs less to treat an alcoholic employee than it does to train someone to take his place after he has been fired. The practical, enlightened view today is that employees must be given an opportunity to undergo treatment. Accept treatment or accept termination is the rule. In the majority of cases of alcoholism referred by industrial medical departments to treatment resources, wonders are worked by consultation and guidance or mild psychiatry or simple medication, once the alcoholic employee has been motivated to accept treatment. Indeed, in the large industries which pioneered industrial alcoholism programs, the recovery rate has been as high as seventy to eighty percent.

There are some employers who grimly cling to an outworn aphorism. "We do not have alcoholic employees; we fire them." Rugged individualism is equated by some of this group with severity and resistance to any changed concept of what alcoholism really is.

In many instances, the findings of neutral arbitrators sitting on union management disputes concerning discharge for alcoholism have given pause to the employers who take the easy way of firing alcoholic employees when their conduct becomes so overt that it is a threat to employee morale. Some of the arbitrator's findings have been far in advance of medical opinion in their insistence that alcoholism is a treatable disease. Arbitrators often have shown the way to a solution in many management-labor disputes.

Also, employers in business and industry have faced the long-term aspect of treating alcoholism and have been largely successful in their efforts. The reasons for this success include that of motivation to save one's job by accepting treatment.

However, employers who have fired alcoholic employees without offering treatment have been given pause by findings of arbitration boards and arbitrators. The two instances cited hereafter are typical.

Alcoholism as a grievance in union-management relationships has been developed by the American Arbitration Association, opening the way for alcoholism programs for employees.

The basic philosophy of arbitrators was formulated by the Rev. John Ford, S.J., the moral theologian, several years ago. He held the view that moral judgments apply only when an alcoholic, given the opportunity and the motivation to accept treatment, continues his drinking behavior in defiance of all reasonable expectations for improvement.

In fewer words, an employee with the diagnosed illness of alcoholism can reasonably expect that opportunity will be given him for treatment and rehabilitation without loss of job or seniority, if he sincerely tries to bring his disorder under control.

Two typical decisions of arbitrators illustrate the views of the arbitrators. One of the cases is that of *Corn Products Company of Kansas City* v. *Oil, Chemical & Atomic Workers International Union.* A question was raised whether an employee, a 52-year-old man, married, father of six children, veteran of World War II, and a master craftsman as a painter, was discharged for just cause. He had frequently volunteered for dangerous "high" painting jobs and was well liked by fellow employees. He had, in fact, been chief steward of his union, representing 725 employees. He was discharged and was unable to find employment because, among other handicaps, he could not get a union card from the Kansas City painters union local. The discharge after 24 years of service was due to alcoholism, which he had attempted without success to control by "on and off" association with Alcoholics Anonymous.

> As is so often the case, [the arbitrator noted] the alcoholic is generally a superior person at his trade, in the office or wherever he is found.
>
> [He went on to observe in the finding] that the illness affecting the employee is not only real, but a treatable one, as attested by the large body of knowledge about alcoholism which has been accumulated in recent years. But, as was the case with other public health problems too, viz., tuberculosis,

cancer, mental illness, there has been considerable lag between the development of such knowledge in the scientific and professional circles and the availability of that information of practical utility at the public level. Such would seem to be the case to a large degree in the present instance.

That alcoholism is a treatable disease or illness has been thoroughly agreed for a number of years by such large groups as the World Health Organization, the American Medical Association, the American Psychiatric Association, the American Hospital Association, a number of health insurance plans, and many others.

That scientific researchers are yet unable to agree upon the underlying causative factors does not reduce the validity of this view, since inability to pinpoint the etiology does not necessarily prevent effective treatment of a number of human ailments. Presently science can only list the causative factors, among them physical, psychological, economic, spiritual and cultural aspects.

Attitudes of industry, based upon the above views expressed by the arbitrator, were summed up in the following, "Alcoholism is not regarded as a disciplinary problem unless or until the individual concerned has been fully informed of the nature of his illness, has been encouraged or directed to seek treatment and refuses such treatment. Then management acts as it could in the case of an employee with active tuberculosis who refuses treatment; it suspends or dismisses the employee."

Note that the employee had tried Alcoholics Anonymous on his own with no beneficial effect because he had, through no fault of AA, been unable to identify himself with the AA program and resisted the notion that he suffered from alcoholism. The arbitrator went on to say, "Simply requiring an alcoholic employee to take effective treatment is not enough to get good, and the desired, result in most cases." The experience of many companies indicates that effective counseling and followup, both by management and union, are important for best results.

The recommended settlement was that the employee should be restored to his job under the following provisions:

He should send a letter in his own handwriting to the personnel manager, agreeing to the following conditions, which, if not kept, would be cause for immediate dismissal:

1. that he abstain from the use of liquor;
2. that he steadfastly adhere to the AA program at one of its local groups;
3. that he comply with company rules, especially with regard to being present at opening and closing times on workdays;
4. that any absenteeism be accounted for with a medical statement from a recognized medical authority;
5. that he follow the course of behavior and treatment agreed upon by union and employer;
6. that he maintain his union activity and avoid trouble with the law that might bring him to unfavorable public attention.

Another decision was that of *American Broadcasting Company* v. *National Association of Broadcast Employees and Technicians.* Melvin Lennard, the impartial arbitrator, found the following concerning the behavior of the employee:

> His deficiencies and offenses, I find, mainly reflect, or are symptoms of, his illness. They establish a deficient work performance record, chiefly in these areas: a high rate of absenteeism and tardiness, frequent failure to notify supervisors in advance of expected long absence, occasional sleeping on the job, and being under the influence of alcohol while on the job. His performance improved substantially between June 5, 1964, when he was given a final warning, and December 25, 1964 (Christmas), when (following the ingestion of six librium capsules and some whiskey) he was extremely drunk and disorderly, suffering a blackout, and interfered obnoxiously and seriously with his employer's operations.

The arbitrator looked at the individual in the round, as an individual rather than a record of employment. He found that if the man were *not* ill his employer would have been justified in firing him. But, he found that the employee had been ill for two years of the four years he had been employed by the network.

> In the light of his illness and in the light of highly disturbing emotional strains, resulting in part from the impending death of his wife and the absence of his 12-year-old daughter, who was in a foster home, not to mention the sometimes acute depression that affects lonely, emotionally disturbed persons on Christmas Day and some other holidays, discharge from his employment would be an excessive penalty for the deficiencies and offenses that are symptoms of his illness. Therefore, there is not now, nor was there on December 28, 1964, just cause for his discharge.

The arbitrator observed that his conclusions would be unwarranted if the employee were not a good risk for regaining his health, arresting the disease, and properly performing his job. This was based, he said, largely upon the insight of a physician who had the employee under treatment.

He found that the employee was not a "classical" alcoholic, by which he meant one who from the first drink responds in an abnormal manner, but that he was a chronic alcoholic (reactive type) who by chronic excessive drinking over a period of two years had "contributed to — and was in a sense partly responsible for acquisition of his present illness."

The recommended disposition of the case was somewhat different than that of the Corn Products case but, again, bore out the thesis that, since the individual could and would cooperate in treatment, the dismissal was an excessive penalty. It was proposed that the dismissal be changed to suspension for a period sufficiently long to permit a reasonable test, under medical supervision and at no cost to the employer, of treatment and recovery. A terminal date was set when the employee, if the conditions agreed upon were met, would be restored to his job with like pay and status and no loss in seniority, but with no vacation for the year.

Periodic reports are to be sent to the company every three weeks by the physician and strict abstinence is to be maintained. If the employee fails to meet the conditions, he may be dismissed.

Finally, it should be observed that the parties went a step beyond usual arbitration powers and granted the arbitrator extraordinary powers to give him authority in this case.

~~~~~~

CHAPTER 7

MODERN TREATMENT
OF ALCOHOLISM

THE WORD INTOXICATION, now commonly used to describe the condition of drunkenness, is a medical contribution to the language. It explains and confirms the understanding of the medical profession of the phenomena resulting from abuse of alcohol. Few doctors today who have scrutinized alcoholics and their symptoms feel that the confirmed alcohol addict is only the slave of a bad habit. They believe, rather, that the long continued abuse of alcohol brings about a diseased condition which results in a craving for the substance that caused the condition and impairs the patient's power to control use of the substance.

Physicians may question how the diseased condition comes about. They speculate whether heredity is a factor, whether the disease is physically or psychologically based, or both. There is controversy about the sort of treatment that will give the greatest relief. But all are agreed that detoxification is the first step in any treatment of alcoholism. As long as the patient continues drinking, a start cannot be made on any of the therapies. The best hope of successful self-control of an alcoholism problem begins with abstinence.

There was a time when detoxification was considered to be

actual treatment of alcoholism, a time when drying out establishments, some ethical but many the instruments of cynical quackery, were said to be administering the "cure" to alcoholics. Today detoxification is generally understood to be only the preliminary step to treatment, not treatment itself.

Detoxification is also somewhat easier today than it was a few decades ago. Alcoholics who either voluntarily or involuntarily are sobered up in a hospital setting or in bed care under controlled conditions are brought through the feared and fearful withdrawal symptoms with very much less physical and psychic pain than the agonies endured when no techniques existed to administer massive doses of vitamins, to use tranquilizing drugs, and to correct dehydration and malnutrition. For many years the single and most widely employed remedy was a shot of paraldehyde which, in effect, prolonged the intoxicated condition, since it is an alcohol derivative. Indeed, it introduced many alcoholics to the possibilities of a paraldehyde binge.

Paraldehyde is a hypnotic and anodyne, a clear liquid of pungent, disagreeable taste and smell, long used to control mania, delirium tremens, tetanus, or morphine poisoning. As some people indulge in a morning-after drink to ease the pangs of a hangover, the acutely intoxicated individual experiences relief from a shot of paraldehyde. The circumstance that the anodyne is suspended in alcohol used to lead to paraldehydism — when alcoholics would switch to the drug because of its swift euphoric action.

Regardless of controversy, modern treatment of alcoholism can be said to have begun with the successful development of the group therapeutic fellowship principles of Alcoholics Anonymous. Such self-discipline, which had glimmered briefly in the Washingtonian movement and waned as that turned into an antiliquor crusade, flared anew as Alcoholics Anonymous, a lay therapy, achieved real recovery and rehabilitation based on a close and noncondemning fellowship.

The Washingtonian movement was founded in Baltimore early in the nineteenth century by a small group of alcoholics who met in taverns to discuss ways and means of freeing themselves from enslavement to drink, as they put it. Supporting one another mutually, the Washingtonian Society gained many adherents, spreading to Boston and New York City. Its principles were not very different at the outset from those espoused very much later by Alcoholics Anonymous. Members gained sobriety, by sharing one another's experiences with liquor. All that remains of the Washingtonian movement today is a hospital in Boston called the Washingtonian Hospital, which began and still continues as a hospital for the treatment of alcoholism. What happened to the Washingtonian Society was that temperance advocates gained control of the society, which, instead of sticking to group therapy to aid alcoholics to control their drinking, turned to anti-liquor crusading.

The debt medicine owes to Alcoholics Anonymous is incalculable. As recently as 1965, thirty years after the formation of Alcoholics Anonymous, a national survey of treatment techniques used in state hospitals admitting alcoholics showed that eighty-eight percent used AA as a "treatment" device, the highest percentage of any of the commonly practiced therapies.

Some profess to see in this fact a rejection of alcoholics as patients by the medical profession, at least insofar as disciplines oriented toward psychiatry are concerned, in that the alcoholics are the only state hospital patients whose "treatment" is entrusted to a lay group, carrying with it the implication that alcoholic patients are worthy of or need nothing better in the way of treatment.

Treatment for alcoholism, over a period of thirty years, has shown a high degree of eclecticism, one eclectic group merging into another with the ideal objective of bringing about earlier and more stable recoveries. The desperate nature of the disease probably accounts for the adaptive and elastic attitudes of treatment disciplines. Try everything; something may work!

In the beginning of the present approach to the disease, treatment centered upon the alcoholic patient. The main effort has been to get the alcoholic sober and, by any means at the command of the healing discipline, to keep the patient sober. It soon became clear that sobriety was often interrupted by environmental factors. The rate of relapse was and still is high. It was also learned that relapse, in itself, is often an important part of the patient's acceptance of the modality. Poor results in treatment, however, are often blamed on an alcoholic patient's "poor" motivation. Yet, rather than motivation, family pressure often triggered relapse.

When many recovered alcoholics joined with the medical profession in the search for the truth about alcoholism, its still undiscovered causes, and its treatment, their experience showed that the process of recovery from alcoholism is to a great extent a process of reeducation of the alcoholics. Even the most highly intelligent patients, of which there seems to be a majority, possess little if any accurate knowledge of how their bodies and minds utilize alcohol, how it is metabolized in the body, and the progressive nature of change from a moderate social drinking to use of alcohol to habitual excess.

To the group at the Yale Center for Alcohol Studies, now shifted to Rutgers, goes credit for shifting the focus of investigation from the narrow limit of the alcoholic's "moral" responsibility to the wider field of the external influences and attitudes surrounding the alcoholic. Not only did the investigators there chart the progressive involvement in alcoholism, but they also developed a structure of environmental and cultural factors in the onset of alcoholism.

Utilizing the life experiences and drinking histories of "recovered" alcoholics in Alcoholics Anonymous, which, although retrospective in nature, provided data available from no other source, the focus on treatment was enlarged to include not only the alcoholic, but his home, his family, his employer, his job, the main sources of the crises which seemed to trigger the drinking episodes of alcoholics. Out of these investigations, several kinds of treatments for alcoholism developed, most of which must be matched to the personality of the patient. This has led to what has been cumbersomely called the multidisciplined approach to alcoholism. More simply it is a "shotgun" technique using all the available disciplines either simultaneously or in succession until the one most suitable and acceptable to the patient is chosen for emphasis, with supportive disciplines utilized as needed.

It has always been essential to provide bed care in any treatment in which the patient comes to a crisis near to the end of a severe drinking episode. The drying-out period is a time when the alcoholic individual, sick and suffering, grasps at almost any straw and, with the best of intentions, professes a desire to stop drinking for good and all. There has always been some exploitation of the need that an alcoholic has for relief of the intolerable distress. Two main techniques were used in "drying-out" sanatoria, health farms, and special alcoholism hospitals. One was an abrupt cutoff of alcohol and a grim bout with withdrawal symptoms, including delirium tremens. The second was a gradual withdrawal of alcohol, called "tapering off." The latter has always been more popular with alcoholics, for the most fearsome symptoms of withdrawal are the constant tremors, sleeplessness, exhaustion, distressing illusions, and hallucinations experienced in the acute stage.

Fear of withdrawal symptoms is frequently an alcoholic's raison d'être for continued and joyless use of alcohol, which is destructive of the frail good intentions and desires to make an effort to stop drinking.

Fear of withdrawal symptoms alone provides no dependable incentive for the alcoholic to shun use of alcohol, for the voice of addiction, whispering from the impaired judgment center of the brain, says, "You can drink again, but this time, carefully, carefully!" For the alcoholic — even with the long-odds gamble that moderation may be within the realm of possibility — there is no strength in "carefully."

Alcoholics Anonymous opened up the feasibility of group therapy and faith healing in its earliest application of mutu-

TABLE 2

The Twelve Steps of Alcoholics Anonymous

1. We admitted we were powerless over alcohol — that our lives had become unmanageable.
2. Came to believe that a Power greater than ourselves could restore us to sanity.
3. Made a decision to turn our will and our lives over to the care of God *as we understood Him.*
4. Made a searching and fearless moral inventory of ourselves.
5. Admitted to God, to ourselves, and to another human being the exact nature of our wrongs.
6. Were entirely ready to have God remove all these defects of character.
7. Humbly asked Him to remove our shortcomings.
8. Made a list of all persons we had harmed, and became willing to make amends to them all.
9. Made direct amends to such people wherever possible, except when to do so would injure them or others.
10. Continued to take personal inventory and, when we were wrong, promptly admitted it.
11. Sought through prayer and meditation to improve our conscious contact with God, *as we understood Him,* praying only for knowledge of His will for us and the power to carry that out.
12. Having had a spiritual awakening as the result of these steps, we tried to carry this message to others, and to practice these principles in all our affairs.

ally supporting discussions in group. Their fellowship, while at first hostile to psychiatry and medication because of the traumatic experiences many of the members had during their search for help, recognized within a very short time that a good part of the effectiveness of the Twelve Steps had been hammered out in group discussion and group experience, and that many of them are based on sound psychiatric principles.

The Twelve Steps of Alcoholics Anonymous (Table 2) have the great merit of being applicable to other life situations in which stress plays a part and in which interpersonal relations suffer from the fact that human beings are somewhat less than divine. Since the largest number of alcoholics have recovered from observing these precepts, they bear reprinting and repetition as frequently as possible.

It has turned out that it is far easier for many alcoholics, perhaps for most of them, to talk out their problems in the midst of a noncondemning group of fellow sufferers, guided by a skillful discussion leader. Often by this means they can come to understanding and a decision to make the effort to recover, rather than hide in singular situations, prey to the corrosive loneliness in our crowded, competitive world.

They learn in groups that their behavioral disorder, which set them apart from the social drinking society where they had failed to conform, is one that will yield without fail to complete abstinence only and that they must open a portal into a new life and new interests.

In the jargon developed around the treatment of alcoholism, the terms "group psychotherapy," "psychochemotherapy," "psychodrama," and all the other compounded words necessary to professional understanding of the psychological aspects of the disease are frequently misinterpreted and often misused. Controversy exists among psychiatrists as to methods, means, and efficacy in dealing with alcoholism. In the space of less than three decades, eclectic psychiatrists have emerged with more solid achievement than the inflexible disciples of Freud, Jung, and Adler in the search for a pathogenic link with the alcoholic's past.

Psychiatrists and internists have long been aware that a large proportion of alcoholics begin treatment only after years of denial, neglect, self-medication, and fruitless efforts to control drinking. They often suffer serious psychiatric disorders, advanced metabolic complications, behavioral changes, and even brain damage if they come to treatment beyond middle age.

Family and community attitudes, too often moralistic and condemning, discourage many physicians who might otherwise take an interest in alcoholic patients. Family and community attitudes brought about recognition by psychiatrically oriented therapists that therapy for alcoholics must go in tandem with therapy for the family. To treatment of alcoholism the psychiatrists, sensitive to the vagaries of human behavior, brought useful application of psychopathology, biochemistry, biophysics, pharmacology, neurophysiology, and sociology.

The use of increasingly sophisticated tranquilizing drugs, giving initial relief from severe anxiety, stress, or agitation, eased the demands upon the time and personal attention of therapists as physicians learned how to manage psychochemotherapy.

The community learns slowly that alcoholics are suffering from a sickness. More and more programs are springing up to provide treatments that utilize the skills of general practitioners as well as specialists, nurses, public health nurses, clergy, social workers, welfare workers, teachers, lawyers, and, as mentioned before, the voluntary efforts of recovered alcoholics.

Psychiatrists not only carried the brunt of the burden in medicine for a long time, but also aroused public concern by outspoken discussion of alcoholism as a health problem. It is significant that American Medical Association policies on alcoholism were developed in the Committee on Mental Health of AMA. It reflects the medical profession's consensus that alcoholism is a behavioral disorder, but not to the exclusion of all other physiological syndromes.

The failure of psychoanalysis to provide significant results in the treatment of alcoholism has been attributed by psychiatrists to the circumstance that probing the subconscious of alcoholics, digging too deeply into the patient's past, creates severe tension and anxiety resulting in recourse by the patient to the use of alcohol. Consequently the eclectic psychiatrist, who concerns himself with the present distress of the patient, seeking ways for the alcoholic to come to terms with the abrasiveness of his present manner of living, has achieved considerable success in treatment of alcoholism. Most important is the fact that psychiatry furnished the needed insight and a reasonable hypothesis to apply existing knowledge to the treatment of alcoholism.

The use of electroshock therapy in treatment of alcoholism for a time gained ascendancy among certain groups of psychiatrists, who used the therapy to treat depression, which occurred in some cases of alcoholism. It was soon discovered, however, that while electroshock was useful in certain kinds of depression, it was far from advantageous as a standard procedure in the treatment of alcoholism. Indeed, in some instances it added to the deterioration incidental in the symptoms of some acute or chronic patients.

Today electroshock treatment is used in some cases of alcoholism, but only in the very limited number which suffer periods of profound depression which cannot be clearly attributed to alcoholism. The fact that memory is impaired by electroshock, at least for a period of time, often inhibits the process of reeducating alcoholics, who do very much better in treatment if they have clear retrospection about how it was with them before they became abstinent.

Thus far no easy pharmacological means has been found to control alcoholism which is not within the means of the alcoholic to subvert. Experience out of the age of the printing press abounds in advertised quack remedies for alcoholism, mostly pills, elixirs, and powders sold to gullible housewives. These nostrums were touted as a means of preventing husbands from drinking by sneaking the stuff into coffee or tea. Other quacks swindled alcoholics with elaborate injections of the salts of precious metals.

There are, however, chemical "fences" which, with cooperation of the patient, have proved very effective in maintaining sobriety. Most notable of these is Disulfiram, a Danish discovery. It is administered to alcoholics in controlled daily doses in pill form and causes a distressing reaction if alcohol is ingested. But, unless the patient takes the prescribed amount of Disulfiram daily, the chemical "fence" is removed, and the patient may relapse into another drinking episode. Similar in its effect is CCC, which has the same properties.

The use of tranquilizers, or psychochemotherapy, in the treatment of alcoholism has shown favorable results in a sufficiently large number of cases to warrant an intensive search by pharmaceutical investigators for improved medications to control the tensions and anxieties of alcoholic patients, as well as those with more clearly defined psychological illnesses. It is quite possible today for the treatment team in a hospital to take a patient through severe withdrawal symptoms to ambulatory condition in the brief time of 72 hours and to reduce the necessary ministration to the patient's acute needs to the point of no more concern than that given to the average minor postsurgical patient. It is done with pharmaceuticals which have been developed within the past two decades, which have proved to leave a minimum risk of chemical side effects.

The abhorrence of "pills" often expressed in the discussions of Alcoholics Anonymous members is, however, justified. Alcoholics are sick people. They have "used" alcohol as a medicine which, to them, seemed effective, even though it made their addiction more severe. To an alcoholic it seems quite simple to exchange addictions. The rationalization of the alcoholics goes somewhat as follows. The alcoholic is pressured to give up alcohol. Very well, the alcoholic says, "I give up alcohol, but I must have pills to substitute for alcohol." The quest for pharmaceuticals for use in treating alcoholics is for nonaddictive compounds which will have no serious side effects but which will also be effective in alleviating physical or psychic distress.

In the main effort to treat alcoholics, the multidisciplined approach has acquired far more adherents than all the others, largely because it rules out none of the others. Too little is known about the causes of alcoholism to rule out even those efforts which have had poor results thus far.

The conditioned reflex treatment, or aversion therapy, has come under attack from the anti-Pavlovians. It has, nevertheless, proved useful with certain types of dependent individuals, who, once conditioned to reject alcohol, walk in fear of it for the remainder of their lives. Conditioned-reflex or aversion therapy can be and usually is quite expensive. It requires considerable time in a closed hospital to administer, and the reflex can be "busted" by an alcoholic who is determined to use alcohol. In substance the aversion treatment consists of a program of giving the patient an emetic or a drug that produces shortness of breath. These cause vomiting or fear each time alcohol is ingested, to the point where the smell, the sight, or even the thought of alcohol causes a severe reaction.

A variation of aversion treatment is electroshock each time alcohol is ingested. There is also an adaptation of the brainwashing techniques developed by the Russian Pavlovians which has been tested behind the Iron Curtain. It consists of administering tranquilizers to alcoholics in group and then bombarding their ears with a repeated lecture of about seventy words over a period of hours every day for over a month. The successful treatments by aversion techniques are far outweighed by the instances in the drinking histories of alcoholics who, to "bust" a conditioned reflex, have choked down repeated shots of liquor in spite of aversion until they no longer vomited or reacted and were able to hold the liquor on their stomachs.

There is kinship here with the patient who only pretends to take Disulfiram because he intends to relapse into alcoholism.

Hypnosis and LSD have been tried in treatment of alcoholism. Both are highly specialized research projects, and the results remain in doubt. In both techniques, public attitudes inhibit extensive research, and among alcoholics there is profound suspicion of anything that passes beyond their conscious volition, except alcohol, which they have come to know very well indeed. The effort to regain personal control has to be the individual's effort.

The secure recovered alcoholic has usually been sober for a very long time before admitting, even to himself, that his recovery is due to some extent to the help that others gave. Therapists are accustomed to hearing alcoholics take the credit themselves for carefully calculated recovery programs. They recognize that only if an alcoholic can take personal responsibility for maintaining sobriety is the sobriety likely to be enduring or secure.

This is probably the central and fundamental value of the multidisciplined technique to aid alcoholics achieve sobriety. All efforts are directed to awakening and utilizing the patient's personal responsibility. Once the subtly introduced ideas are in action, the therapist can choose a tactful moment to step aside and introduce fresh responsibilities in other departments of the individual's life.

The sequence of treatment has been drastically revised during the past two decades. The alcoholic today is rarely the first person seen in connection with treatment. Case finding depends to a great extent upon educational and information efforts directed at families and employers of alcoholics. The first contact with a premotivational resource in alcoholism is made most often by a family member or by an employer.

What must first be determined is whether the alcoholic has accepted the fact that a problem with alcohol exists and then how best to acquaint the individual with the true state of affairs.

If the individual accepts referral and introduction to a group of Alcoholics Anonymous, the first effort is made in that direction. But many reject AA at first, dismissing it as "a bunch of evangelists," or "a lot of con men," or some such immature judgment. It is at this point that family and employer counseling is vital. Families have usually watched the development of an alcoholism problem without comprehension of what is going on before their eyes. Wives, for example, have been known to observe alcoholism in a husband for five to ten years before they became fully aware of the problem.

Family counseling is necessary for several reasons. One of the most important is that family members have to be instructed to keep hands off the alcoholism problem in order to let it be worked out between the treatment discipline and the alcoholic. This often includes the creation of a crisis that may spark the alcoholic's acceptance of the problem.

More and more employers are discovering that it is worth dollars and cents to them to cooperate in treatment of an alcoholic employee, simply because treatment is far cheaper than replacement. The employer also controls one of the most important motivations — the job. Earlier case findings and earlier treatment have shown that the employed alcoholic, who has been given a clear and concise statement of the terms on which the job can be retained, does far better in recovery than one given warnings that are without force or effect.

Once the family and employer are informed and aware of

the why and wherefore of alcoholism treatment, the first phase of multidiscipline treatment begins, drying out. This is also true of the single disciplines. It is important that all concerned understand the complexities of treatment. Otherwise, bungling through ignorance is a constant threat.

The next effort is to break down the denial symptom — the rationalization by which the alcoholic presents to the world an "almost" persuasive denial of an alcoholism problem. This is usually the function of a counselor, a psychologist, a discussion leader in a group, a social worker, or a physician. The denial syndrome may be evidenced in several ways. Some alcoholics will declare stoutly that they can handle the problem themselves. The person counseling then makes a bargain — the alcoholic will be given a chance to handle it but, failing, then will accept prescribed treatment procedures.

Through the entire period of treatment every effort is made to maintain contact with the patient, to be noncondemning, and to encourage discussion of the problem. Therapists never actually give any ground to the specious arguments of the alcoholic, but strive to communicate information about the disease, the way in which the body actually utilizes alcohol, the symptoms of alcoholism, and the advantage of not attempting to change too much in their lives too rapidly.

Pastoral counseling is often necessary to bridge the spiritual gap left as the alcoholic becomes obsessed with guilt feelings and moral insecurity. In establishing rapport, clergymen have learned not to preach at alcoholics, not to pass moral judgments, but to act as friendly counselors, interceding in the many areas of life in which the clergy can exert influence.

Pastoral counseling is achieving a new and quite dynamic role in the treatment of alcoholism. The success is due to a very small group of theologians who grasped the significant fact that alcoholics have for several centuries been the targets and victims of the unjust moral outrage of their coreligionists. Not until Father Ford and the Rev. Howard J. Clinebell, Jr., a psychologically trained clergyman, had given intensive study to alcoholism, were benchmarks established to limit the moral judgments generally prevailing regarding alcoholics. Father Ford held that the moral wrong, the label of sin, should be applied only to alcoholics who persistently and consciously refused treatment for the sickness. The Rev. Mr. Clinebell argued that clergymen erred in preaching at alcoholics instead of understanding and counseling them with the techniques of applied religion and psychology.

Such public declarations as that of the General Board of the National Council of Churches opened up a new vista for pastoral counseling of alcoholics. The National Council held that clergy and churches should recognize that once drinking passes a certain point it becomes alcoholism and that alcoholics then need diagnosis, understanding, guidance — and are especially in need of pastoral care and the divine love the church can bring them.

A growing number of treatment disciplines have pastoral counselors on their staffs whose function it is to provide guidance and counsel, not to lecture or preach. In short, clergymen are now participating in treatment, not merely directing alcoholics to treatment centers.

The treatment team used in most disciplines today includes physicians, psychiatrists, psychologists, social workers, nurses, clergymen, and counselors. The latter, having maintained contact with all the elements of the problem, may be either recovered alcoholics or trained social workers; they develop a special sensory perception to anticipate and head off crises.

Multidisciplined treatment does not end when the patient has maintained stability for a certain number of weeks or months. There are other problems — such as having the normal social and business functions of the individual, which have been taken over by others during his illness, restored to the recovered alcoholic. He must learn how to live and move normally in a social drinking society without participating in the drinking. More will be said in another chapter about sustaining sobriety.

The defects of the available treatment resources are numerous. There are not enough trained personnel to staff necessary treatment resources. The attitude of the community, which, in the end, has to foot the bill for failure to cope with alcoholism as a health problem, is not yet favorable to broadening the base of treatment. Hospitals are responding very slowly to the need for treating alcoholism as they would treat any other disease. Follow-up of patients after hospitalization is neglected, and too much reliance is placed upon a few months of sobriety to effect what people call "a cure."

Therapeutic techniques are in most cases empirical but, regardless, are capable of a significantly large percentage of success. Successful industry programs on alcoholism, utilizing the best services for treatment in the community, have shown recovery percentages as high as eighty percent, based on ten-year follow-up studies. Finally, Alcoholics Anonymous, which is by far the most frequently used after-care or reinforcement resource, can call the roll of hundreds of thousands of recovered alcoholics.

In summary, one can be assured that abstinence is generally regarded as a necessary first step in treatment and that continued success in remaining abstinent reinforces the alcoholic's self-confidence. The loneliness and isolation of the alcoholic is replaced by gradually improving relations with his social group. He reenters the world of normal association with others with the ability to bear the periods of tension and low esteem which are natural in a competitive society.

Therapists often remark that it is doubtful if recovered alcoholics ever really give up a secret hope that someday, by some miracle of regeneration of their cells or some trick of the enzyme system, they will be able to drink again, so powerful is the hold that alcohol exerts over a social drinking society.

The choice of treatments is very hard, except as to availability. Alcoholics recover in many different ways, largely because each case of alcoholism is unique, similar to others only in the basic addiction. No matter what treatment discipline is chosen, the alcoholic is not likely to recover if he persists in defending his denial of the problem against all reasonable proof of the existence of an alcoholism problem. For this reason alcoholics in treatment are surrounded by knowledgeable people who bring to bear massive pressure, without any outward show of force, to break down the barrier of denial. The therapist chooses a time when denial is weakest to move in and demolish the defenses.

Those who have spent significant effort on therapy for alcoholics develop a sixth sense which makes it possible for them to spot the time when the alcoholic will be most receptive to surrender of the denials. They feel no sense of victory over an obdurate adversary, realizing that they have much to do before the patient will achieve secure sobriety.

The chief objective in treatment is to make a beginning and to bring the alcoholic to heed the still, small voice in his consciousness that has been saying for a long time that something is gravely wrong.

~~~~~~

CHAPTER 8

THE BRIDGE TO FUTURE SOBRIETY

AT SOME TIME in the recovery process, the problems of adjustment to a new way of life come to a junction point, where the recovering alcoholic either begins development of a personal attitude towards abstaining or adopts the guidelines of the therapeutic discipline chiefly responsible for recovery.

Something more than blindly following rules of behavior will make it possible to avoid drinking and thus avoid relapse. More accurately, it is development of a sort of spiritual intuition transcending ordinary understanding — a mysticism which buffers the individual against all assaults on personal tranquility.

When Alcoholics Anonymous went through the process of developing a mystique, the founders leaned very heavily on two published works — James' *Varieties of Religious Experience* and Courtenay Baylor's *Remaking a Man*. On reading these books, one is immediately impressed by the need that recovered alcoholics have for a powerful personal spiritual experience through which they can reach into infinity and retain powerful hold on what Alcoholics Anonymous, in an inspired phrase, calls a "Power greater than themselves."

If recovery from alcoholism were merely a matter of learning by rote the rules to serve as a behavioral guide to abstain from the use of alcoholic beverages, the need for personal adjustment to a new way of life would not be of great importance. In previous chapters, however, there has been reference to an almost overpowering need of the alcoholic to believe that the meaningful thoughts and actions used in rationalizing a nonalcoholic manner of living are his own, that he has found recovery on his own, and that sobriety is *his* unassisted personal achievement. There follows after this feeling of individual achievement a need for something more — a spiritual experience relevant to control of the alcoholic's behavioral disorder, which must be personal enough to restore and expand the metaphysical experience of youth before the individual lost contact with a religious connection. At first this is a feeling, and then a conviction, that he is not alone in his progress toward recovery; that he is being helped by people of faith and understanding; that a power of selflessness is at work for his personal benefit. With this spark of insight, the individual begins to believe and use his new-found power. At this point he sheds his aggression and becomes more objective in his outlook.

Without knowing or caring what is the source of the Serenity prayer, a great majority of alcoholics carry it around with them and think about it, without recognizing that it is a tiny anchor for their mysticism in a vast troubled sea of doubt, and that from it they derive new insights and reinforcement of their mystique. Believed to be derived from a prayer by St. Francis of Assisi and rendered into modern idiom by Reinhold Niebuhr, the prayer says, simply, "God grant me the serenity to accept the things I cannot change, the courage to change the things I can, and the wisdom to know the difference. Amen."

In a way it is a self-centered prayer, for it asks for personal acquisition of serenity, courage, and wisdom. Yet, it is peculiarly suited to the discipline necessary to controlling a disease marked by a high intensity of self-centeredness. To the recovering alcoholic who hasn't been able to bow to formal religion in contrition and humility, the notion of a Power greater than himself, of a prayer asking for serenity, courage, and wisdom, offers hope of a profound personal religious experience, almost a conversion.

Not all recovering alcoholics go through the conversion experience and its shattering revelation of personal inadequacy to cope with the overmastering tyranny of liquor. Some never have the conversion experience; some meet it very early in their striving for recovery, but most find that the desired serenity, courage, and wisdom is gained bit by bit, as they adjust to the sobriety that is necessary and the outlook that is lofty and serene.

One of the best illustrations of the state of mind and the viewpoint of recovered alcoholics seeking to develop personal attitudes of reorientation to life is a conversation with an actress noted in the theatre for the competitive ruthlessness with which she sought and commanded recognition. She had also an acute drinking problem. As she recovered from alcoholism she was aware that she had hurt many people, but her drive would not permit her to relax her competitive zeal. Then she adopted the Catholic faith and, in her piety, mellowed considerably. One day, after having been in the confessional, she was approached by a director with an offer to replace another actress in a coveted part.

"No, no," she said. "Do not talk to me now about that. I am in a state of grace. I want to find out if I can maintain it."

Like the actress in the state of grace, the alcoholic feels a moment of exaltation, a brief exaltation experienced without the use of alcohol, and clings to it, analyzes it, strives to repeat the circumstances which brought it about and thus formulates a spiritual discipline of his own, bit by bit, collecting these moments of grace until at last the serenity, courage, and wisdom so ardently desired are his. He is able to accept himself, able to forgive himself (very different from excusing himself for derelictions), and to understand at last how to live above the turmoil and stress of a competitive materialistic civilization.

Development of this personal attitude, this mystical belief in one's intuitive powers to recognize and act upon threats to sobriety, is quite often threatened when one's sobriety is undermined by external influences. Even events outside of one's control can have a profound effect on alcoholics, even those who seem most secure.

For reasons which have not been thoroughly studied and analyzed, many alcoholics relapsed during the days that followed the assassination of President Kennedy. The subliminal motivation most often recounted by those who relapsed at this time was that they felt a wave of hopelessness, an enveloping and stifling emotion which left them asking themselves the question, "What's the use?" Political partisanship had nothing to do with the feeling, they explained. It was a sudden recognition that tragedy can overtake a person as vital and admirable as the young President who symbolized for many the realization of youth's most valiant dreams of achievement.

Several years ago, an article about alcoholism and Alcoholics Anonymous was printed in a national magazine. The premise of the article was that Alcoholics Anonymous was in danger of becoming an evangelistic religion, rather than a lay healing discipline. It was quite destructive for many men and women who owed their sobriety to long and close affiliation with AA. One agonized old timer telephoned for advice.

"What shall I do?" he said. "This man attacks the things I believe in — the things I found out for myself, the things I depend upon to stay sober and to maintain serenity."

He was advised to write a letter to the author, to mince no

words, to abuse him if he felt that way, to say everything he had to say in disagreement.

"But, I have been living above that kind of thing," he protested.

"Then, after you have written the letter, tear it up and think no more about it." Days later the man called again.

"It worked," he said cheerfully. "I got it out of my system."

Getting "it" out of one's system looms large in the exercise of an alcoholic's personal attitude, the use of an intuitive spiritual solvent to maintain serenity, or tranquility. Maintenance of an even temper, an even effort, and the strict control of feelings of hostility are much more important to people with a behavioral disorder than to a person who has become intuitively adjusted to the uneven abrasiveness of modern life. Resentments, often allowed by alcoholics to become a bitter brew, have to be carefully examined and reevaluated. The rules and precepts of such disciplines as Alcoholics Anonymous can be utilized to ease the alcoholic individual past the routine threats to serenity, but by far the greater number of personal problems cannot be handled by a predetermined formula. With the old problem solver unavailable, the average alcoholic is under pressure to find solutions which are not capable of formula answers. From this comes the advantage of association with a group of recovered alcoholics. Someone in the group may have the answer as the problem is talked out.

In order to develop a personal attitude governing sobriety and to develop a personal spiritual intuition, the ideal regimen seems to be association with a group of recovered alcoholics, so that a talking relationship is maintained, but not to the extent of complete dependency upon group support. Alcoholism can become a numbing bore if it is the only conversational gambit of an individual. To a large extent adjustment of a personal attitude — a mystique beneficial to control of alcohol problems — depends upon broadening one's interests, which also helps to discover dormant talents. These talents can then be developed, giving one new incentives for living.

Alcoholics are often aghast at the extent to which their thinking has been limited to the subject of alcohol, ranging from what kind of beverage, the time they start drinking, the uses of alcohol, the need for alcohol, the role of alcohol in their lives. This realization of an alcohol-centered existence comes during the recovery phase, but its deeper meaning is appreciated only when the alcoholic is able to stop thinking during every waking minute of how to abstain from alcohol and what to substitute for alcohol.

Not until social drinkers become aware of the almost total preoccupation of an alcoholic with drinking will the process of recovery from alcoholism be understood. Not until this understanding is achieved will the public comprehend the alcoholic's need to substitute something to fill the void left in his life by sobriety. The coffee-drinking recovered alcoholic often flaunts his preference for a cup of coffee as a proud symbol of his sobriety; but the extent to which coffee has been used as a substitution — and a necessary substitution — is little understood by people who are not alcoholics.

Nonalcoholics are often shocked by the fact that alcoholics are amused by some of the most tragic episodes in their drinking history, particularly when there is a burst of laughter while an alcoholic is giving testimony about personal drinking behavior in a group discussion. This brotherhood of ironic laughter, however, is therapeutic; for only in this way are alcoholics able to contemplate with equanimity the ingredients of their despair. Very often the essentials of the "surrender" or "conversion" process necessary to recovery may be found in these grimly amusing tales out of drinking histories.

One of the most shattering experiences out of a personal

recollection is that of a man who had been the class poet in his Ivy League college, who, living in the shadow of a great and famous father, had become an alcoholic, often to the embarrassment of his famous parent. With the death of his father the alcoholic was entrusted with the task of carrying his father's ashes back to America from abroad for interment in the family lot. He staggered off a transatlantic plane, intoxicated and tremulous, lurched through customs, and went on a wobbling run for the airport bar. He tripped, fell, and dropped the urn with the ashes. The package burst and his father's ashes were strewn over the airport main lobby. Porters were summoned. The ashes were gathered as best they could be and handed to him in a paper bag. This is the way he arrived home, beset by the reproaches of relatives and formally expelled from the family at the family lawyer's reading of his father's will, which left him only a small bequest. But, outrageous as this experience may seem, it had a profound effect on the alcoholic. Afterward he spoke of it.

"There on the floor of the lobby in the airport, scrambling around trying to protect my father's ashes from the hurrying feet of the passengers, it suddenly occurred to me at long last, 'I am not in his shadow any longer. Here he is — looking no different than the dust on the floor of this public place. He's gone and I have to be myself in my own way.' " He began to build a personal mystique in that moment and within months was securely sober, a sobriety that lasted the rest of his life.

Traumatic experiences while alcoholics are drinking, and even more painful experiences when they are striving to get sober, often require more adjustment than rationalization. Men and women who lose their spouses and their children, who never win their way back into the social group to which they belonged, men and women who must make new lives and develop new interests, often find this part of recovery even more trying than the self-discipline required to remain sober. Yet, there are few traumatic experiences of alcoholics which do not yield to frank discussion. The truly courageous step may be to extricate one's self from an unsuitable marriage, from an onerous and hated way of earning one's livelihood, from a milieu of dull conformity to boring social standards, and not to attempt to go back to the way one was following when the drinking problem began.

Some recovered alcoholics learn the hard way that recovery from the disease is not penance ad infinitum. After sincere and reasonable attempts to make amends for any wrong they may have done, their obligation is to themselves. This doesn't mean self-righteousness, but a carefully thought out effort to restore in themselves the spiritual and moral values by which they reinforce their sobriety and their security. As this change in attitude and action takes place, many alcoholics say, "I am now becoming a member of the human race."

There are family members to be found who persist in demanding continual penance from the recovered alcoholic, who have no comprehension that the recovered alcoholic has not taken vows in a penitential order, but rather has entered upon a new life after having been prisoner of an addiction. In such situations the family relationships are often terminated for the good of all, for such destructive attitudes can cause more damage than a sensitive individual can tolerate.

Gratitude for the support given to an alcoholic can also go past the bounds of reasonable spiritual recognition. There are wives, for example, who resent the growth of a personal mystique in a recovered alcoholic. They feel excluded, deprived of what they conceive to be their just due of gratitude from the alcoholic. They feel that the sobriety is the result almost solely of their understanding and forbearance. Martyrdom, whether outwardly expressed or inwardly implied, has given such wives a sick satisfaction. They behave as if the alcoholic is a naughty child suddenly become well behaved but resentful of restraints.

Where such relationships exist, recovered and recovering alcoholics need not only the guidance of an experienced person who will point out ways of arbitrating the clash of personal viewpoints, but also acceptance of the fact that if the differences cannot be ironed out, it could be best for sobriety's sake to terminate the relationship.

Fortunately, in these times, when intervention in alcoholism comes very much earlier in the course of the disease, there are not so many hard decisions to make. Families have more to save, more mutual interests, and more desire to let bygones be bygones, grateful for the solution of what might have become a tragic problem. Many spouses and children of alcoholics are pleasantly surprised by the change in their lives and the change in the disposition of the alcoholic — very often the completely new mystique. The new person revealed by the development of a new personality is often far more attractive than the prealcoholic individual had been.

There are some instances, however, in which the recovered alcoholic becomes dour and introspective — a gloomy raincloud hovering over a household. Some wives have expressed it this way:

"I liked him better when he was drinking. Now he is a constant grouch."

One has to pay careful attention to what this means. What the wife usually means is that she is reluctant to give back to the husband the role of husband and head of the household. On the other hand, the dour grouch may not as yet have begun development of broadened interests to substitute for alcohol. He may be inwardly listening to a babel of voices from other times and in other rooms. He may need only time and understanding to develop a new outgoing personality. For the alcoholic, this is a convalescent period.

Alcoholics in time learn by intuition to take evasive action when threatened by tension, anxiety, and stress. They consciously slow down, pace themselves to tackle one thing at a time, identify the nature of the thing that is causing them to have unquiet feelings or feelings of dis-ease.

This inventory taking becomes almost automatic in many recovered alcoholics. They have a sort of barometer built in and measuring the pressure. When storm signals are flown, when they find themselves becoming the center of a circular whirl of emotion, they know how to get out of it, how to avoid being swept away.

One can declare, with the substance of experience of many recovered alcoholics to back up the statement, that the development of the mystical intuition that comes with the spiritual surrender or conversion actually creates a new individual, one with the old skills and talents, so often unused or abused, channeled into dynamic development of a new personality and a more effective individual.

~~~~~~

CHAPTER 9

ANATOMY OF AN
ALCOHOLIC RELAPSE

IT SOMETIMES HAPPENS that a recovered alcoholic has had several years of sobriety and then, quite unexpectedly, a "slip" or relapse occurs. Family, friends, and colleagues may wag their heads mournfully and comment in tones ranging from compassionate to sanctimonious, "Once a drunk, always a drunk."

There are different reasons for relapse, some of which can be recognized in advance and headed off. The more comprehension the alcoholic has of why alcoholism gained a foothold in the first place, the less likelihood there is that he will relapse.

First of all, it must be recognized that alcohol, for the alcoholic, has greater personal rewards than it has for the average social drinker. It has in most cases been the "medicine" that worked faster and, for a short term, more effectively than any other. True, it is the wrong medicine. In treating themselves with this medicine to suppress fears, anxiety, tension, timidity — all of the many-faced bugaboos of alcoholism — alcoholics had (to quote the old phrase) fools for physicians.

To achieve sobriety is a very real struggle for an alcoholic. Every fibre of one's being resents and rejects this effort to cut off the use of alcohol. In making the effort, the alcoholic expects, quite reasonably, some sort of reward other than the improvement of health and brighter prospects as a person with a more mature outlook and improved judgment.

If the reward for the herculean effort to achieve sobriety fails to come up to expectations, alcoholics will sometimes go back to drinking. The failure in this case arises from expecting more than is reasonable as a reward for sobriety, and, manifestly, it arises also from the failure of the responsible counselor to spell out true and valuable rewards of sobriety in terms that the alcoholic can understand and accept. More specifically, however, the failure is rooted in the demands of the family, friends, or colleagues for a flashing, brilliant performance from the recovered alcoholic almost immediately upon achieving a long period of sobriety. It just doesn't work that way. It took a long time for the alcoholic to become sick enough to require strict sobriety as the only alternative, and it will take a long time for the alcoholic to become secure enough to face up to rebuffs, disappointment, tensions, etc.

When two or three months of sobriety have been achieved and when a glow of satisfaction is felt at having been able to control the drinking problem, the environment of the alcoholic in the recovery stage may breed relapses for reasons which are not immediately recognized and accepted by members of the family.

A. ROLE IN THE FAMILY. During the development of the serious involvement in alcoholism, the alcoholic's role in the family has changed. Family functions once assigned to the alcoholic have been taken over by some other family member. In the case of a husband and father, the duties once borne by the head of the house are taken over by the wife or older children or have been poorly performed by the alcoholic. The question often is not when alcoholics can resume those family functions, but whether they will be permitted to resume them. The housewife whose drinking problem has shattered the orderly routine of her household often finds that it is difficult to pick up the threads again.

B. JOB FRUSTRATION. The alcoholic whose job has been changed to something with less prestige and satisfaction, who is faced with a long pull of rehabilitation, often becomes discouraged and frustrated as he seeks to erase those two destructive labels, often a reflection of the stigma on the disease, "Has been" and "Never was."

C. SOCIAL LIFE. The alcoholic must often search for a new and acceptable social group when relationships with old social drinking friends have become awkward, both because of avoiding drinking situations and because old friends are ill at ease. The old group is often unconsciously hostile to one who has been unable to stand the pace, hold his liquor, or play the social drinking game according to their rules.

D. REBUFFS. Accumulations of rebuffs, fancied slights, tactless remarks about abstinence often leave the alcoholic feeling miserable and left out, ending with his saying: "I might as well be drunk as the way I am."

E. OVERBURDEN. A majority of nonalcoholics have the erroneous belief that all an alcoholic has to do to be completely rehabilitated and rejuvenated is to stop drinking. This results in demands upon alcoholics far in excess of their capabilities at the earlier stages of sobriety.

F. OVERCONFIDENCE. The recovered alcoholic may be overconfident that, after an extended period of sobriety, he has made it and can get along without maintaining constant vigilance against threats to his sobriety.

G. REMEMBRANCE OF THE PAST. The alcoholic may have an inability to let the past go, with all its unhappiness and distress, and he may fail to have compassion for himself.

H. DRY DRUNKS. The so-called "dry" drunk is experienced by many recovered alcoholics. It is an almost complete, but usually temporary, recurrence of the active symptoms of compulsive drinking without ever having had a drink of alcohol, carrying with it a keenly aroused feeling that one has only to take a drink to be rid of the suddenly unbearable tensions and anxieties. Secure recovered alcoholics usually draw closer to their AA affiliation, their sponsor, their physician, or counselor to get past the "dry" drunk and stay sober and abstinent.

I. SELF-PITY.

J. SEDUCTION. In some instances the mates of recovered alcoholics will by their own attitudes, and often with deliberate intent, seduce alcoholics to drink again because they preferred them dependent and immature and resent their growing independence and firm convictions after recovery. Wives and husbands frequently enjoy wearing the crown of martyrdom and their dearly earned reputations for bearing up under the handicap of a drunken husband or wife.

*   *   *

These are a few of the areas in the anatomy of alcoholic relapse which are rarely discussed by the family, friends, and associates of recovered alcoholics and are seldom understood. Even recovered alcoholics, in their striving to regain a secure place in the society, the environment, and the culture of their time, often overlook the menace of the postrecovery situations that threaten their sobriety. One of the reasons why Alcoholics Anonymous is a continuing fellowship is that recovered alcoholics have a need to talk out the threats to their sobriety with those who understand and share their concern.

Recovery and rehabilitation in alcoholism are only halfway home when the alcoholic has been able to maintain as long as two years of sobriety. The alcoholic man or woman completes the journey to security when he or she learns how to head off threats to his sobriety inherent in his associations with nonalcoholic people, interaction with people, and the uncertainties of his own mind.

Any consideration of a relapse must take into account the elements that went into the decision of the alcoholic to stop drinking. The dynamic force of this decision must be understood and admired. An alcoholic is usually a person in subnormal physical and psychological condition, who knows better than anyone else that withdrawal of alcohol is going to mean that the pain and distress which has caused the drinking will be even less bearable — at least for a period of time. Nevertheless, the alcoholic makes the decision to stop. Those who think that an alcoholic lacks will power should ponder these facts.

Improvement of the physical, psychic, economic, and social conditions is seldom immediate or sudden, although the alcoholic begins to feel better, to obtain some small rewards for sobriety. But what is impressed upon the alcoholic most forcefully is that the recovery and rehabilitation process is going to be a long-term effort. The alcoholic in the process of recovery is beset by insistent temptation to drink because of tension, restlessness, gusts of hostility and irritability. Often fogs of despondency sweep in, and no one seems to comprehend the alcoholic's need for the clasp of a firm and confident hand to lead the way out of the depressed state.

While the recovery process gathers strength and force, the alcoholic is learning that it is virtually impossible to go it alone. Help of the right kind is necessary, and it must be available when the alcoholic needs it. If it isn't available, a relapse is threatened. However, frequently the relapse is an important part of the process of recovery, because many alcoholics test their ability to control drinking after learning something about the disease of alcoholism.

To avoid relapse one must look inward and guard against six mental blocks. These are resentment, jealousy, self-pity, procrastination, stupidity, and self-doubt.

Self-doubt, centered upon confidence in one's own abilities, may take several forms. There is doubt about ability to keep up with competition. If it is in business, it may be a younger colleague, associate, or co-worker who arouses self-doubts by seeming to perform with greater ease. In personal and social activities, one may indulge in invidious comparisons with the popularity of a neighbor, a friend, an acquaintance, a political figure. A wife may even seem more capable of making friends, attracting attention to her skills and her achievements, leaving the alcoholic husband to seem commonplace and unimportant.

Some envious people are unable to analyze their jealousy of others. They tear people apart, criticize and belittle the achievements of others, probe for a weak spot in others to salve their own ego. A certain amount of this is a part of everyone's behavior, but alcoholics develop the techniques of character assassination to a fine art. Then, when sober, they use their better judgment to analyze their own faults, and sometimes this self-analysis is painful and may precipitate another drinking episode.

Alcoholics tend to put off the serious thinking they should do today until tomorrow or to some time in the future when the signs are more propitious. Tomorrow, when they are going to start thinking seriously, is too often postponed indefinitely. The plans to take a course, improve one's skills, turn over a new leaf, make amends for old wrongs, and think charitably of all fellow humans are written in the moisture on the glass containing a long cold drink. Essential judgment is impaired by the drink, and nothing gets accomplished.

Often an alcoholic feels the need for help, but feels too proud to ask for help and wishes vaguely that someone would detect his need and provide the answers. He rationalizes in such instances that he is misunderstood, isolated, rejected. He does not realize that to ask for help is one way of assuring others that they are useful which enlists the very best effort of those giving the help.

Many alcoholics neglect a physical checkup, thinking that

all they are required to do is give up drinking. Checkups often disclose some slight physical malfunction which can be corrected easily — often by vitamin supplements or dietary supplements of iron-bearing foods.

Rigid ideas are unacceptable to others, and stubborn efforts of the alcoholic on the verge of relapse to force family, friends, associates, fellow workers to accept such ideas often cause relapse. What the alcoholic has attempted is to force others to change their thinking out of a need to appear superior. When such domineering is rejected, the alcoholic easily convinces himself that acquaintances, family associates, and fellow workers are not the considerate friends they pretend to be. He forgets that friendship, love, and consideration for others are selfless. When others respond to achievement, to ideas, and to basic attitudes, such response has been earned, not acquired as a right, by staying sober and only that.

Change is not easy, but it can come about faster and more securely for the alcoholic if the following rules are followed:

FIRST, recognize the need to change.

SECOND, muster a little courage to make the effort.

THIRD, make resolves and keep them to one's self, unless doubt prompts a need for wise counsel.

FOURTH, anyone can manage to change if he tries, and he could be surprised by what is achieved when a sincere effort to change is made.

FIFTH, once past the first hurdle of really making the effort to change, all succeeding obstacles are easier to surmount, and the alcoholic is on his way back to join the human race, understanding that it is a race in more meanings than one.

1. The relapse should not be used (A) to justify or excuse the patient's drinking; (B) to scold or put other condemning pressure on the patient; (C) to give up efforts to help the patient achieve permanent sobriety.

2. Usually relapse is preceded by a build-up of tension or anxiety, sometimes an accumulation of petty annoyances.

The alcoholic can head off the relapse by talking it out with an understanding and unemotional person, preferably a stable member of Alcoholics Anonymous, a trained therapist, a physician, a clergyman, or a trusted friend whose opinion is valued.

3. Both voluntary and public agencies, working on problems of alcoholism, understand and cooperate with the sober alcoholic who experiences tension or anxiety and needs to talk it out. An important part of the work of voluntary committees and councils on alcoholism is helping alcoholics, their friends, relatives, and employers to understand and cooperate in recovery after a relapse or to head off a relapse.

4. Family members should familiarize themselves with the vague signs and symptoms that precede a relapse and help to make sobriety more rewarding and vital for the alcoholic.

5. Employers should anticipate that relapse may occur and should know enough about alcoholism so that action taken is not either too punitive or too complacent. The alcoholic employee values his job, and this often proves very important in heading off a relapse.

6. The alcoholic should not hesitate to seek supportive help when tensions, anxiety, and the petty annoyances become unbearable.

7. When he tries to drink socially once again, the alcoholic should be aware of the difference between "experimentation" drinking, or "nipping," and the true relapse. This important step may mean the difference between successful recovery and continued compulsive drinking.

8. Alcoholism is a disease and, as with any other disease, relapses sometimes interrupt recovery. If a diabetic experiences a diabetic coma, remedial action is taken. If the tubercular patient experiences a recurrence of active tuberculosis, intensive treatment is resumed. The relapse in alcoholism also requires treatment of a kind which, because the patient is usually well motivated, is much easier to administer than treatment on the alcoholic's first contact with therapy.

9. Relatives should avoid feelings of hopelessness or despair or any expression to the alcoholic of such feelings.

10. At the first signs of unrest, do something about it, something besides hoping that all the threats to sobriety may adjust themselves.

Blinding revelations of spiritual conversion or acts of surrender are experienced by some recovered alcoholics, but most have to strive for and think about the means of achieving stability and tranquility and constantly have to maintain alertness against any emotional threat to their new way of life.

Too often alcoholics misinterpret the references to spiritual rebirth which they hear from a counselor, at an AA meeting, or from a psychiatrist. They have often been through traumatic experiences while drinking, which have had the effect of permanently putting a barrier between them and formal practice of a religion. They have residual feelings of unworthiness when confronted with the frequent references to "God as we understand Him," "a Power greater than ourselves," and "humbly asking Him to remove our shortcomings" and "having a spiritual awakening," which are found in the Twelve Steps of Alcoholics Anonymous. Often these feelings of unworthiness before God result in conscious avoidance of any association with AA. On the other hand, a very great number of alcoholics seeking recovery do have so-called spiritual awakenings, quite as effective as those achieved in the AA discipline. They acquire this spiritual reinforcement through a sublimation of their intense ethical striving for worthiness, stability, and self-control. Theologians may attribute this spiritual awakening to God's intervention, but one cannot discount the therapeutic effect of a deep commitment to self-help of the alcoholic individual. The fact is that many agnostics recover from alcoholism and maintain their sobriety from a spiritual awakening.

Until very recently, pastoral counseling was not conspicuously successful as a therapy in alcoholism, largely because alcoholics as a group were (and often still are) resentful or apprehensive of being "preached at." More recently, pastoral counseling for alcoholics has acquired a new sophistication, which depends more upon a psychological than a prayerful approach to the alcoholic. This sophistication is largely due to the entry into sobriety of a significantly large number of clergymen of many faiths after alcoholic episodes of extraordinary severity. These men have, over the course of the past decade, resolutely directed their efforts to a revision of the clergyman's image or stereotype held by the majority of alcoholics.

It is highly significant that these pioneering pastoral counselors have been content to let the credit for spiritual awakening of alcoholics go where it may, serene in the knowledge that, whatever the cause for this inner tranquility and stability, alcoholics have become very much better people — often better than they were before alcoholism entered their lives.

The evangelical fervor, the Bible pounding, the exhortation to repentence are now old hat in the field of alcoholism. Even the good works of Skid Row missions are questioned, for it has been demonstrated that the alcoholic who pays for his bed and board, as the Chinese "Rice Christians" did, by listening to hymns and sermons has gained very little in the fight against alcoholism. Indeed, in far too many cases it has taken the fight out of them and made them even more dependent.

The outcome of spiritual awakening and its importance as a mainstay of recovered alcoholics is, in the great majority of cases, a mellowing of aversion to religion and eventual acceptance of a religious affiliation. They come at last to understand that the experience of spiritual awakening is not what is of greatest importance, but what they do with it after it happens.

One can learn a great deal about the enormous diversity

of beliefs and of what the spiritual awakening means by talking to recovered alcoholics. In general, those who have had
the most traumatic experiences in efforts to control their
disease without recourse to help of others are quick to recognize that there is a mystery about the source from which they
derived their recovery and that if they question themselves
too much about that source they can get into a quagmire of
doubt. The rationalizations about the Power greater than
themselves can assume a host of fanciful shapes. Behavioral
sciences wisely shun probing too deep beneath the surface of
these beliefs.

Neutral observers, studying recoveries from alcoholism,
see only the change. They will remark, "He's a changed man,"
or, "She's a new woman." And they do not make a great effort
to pinpoint the source, the terms, or the philosophy of the
spiritual awakening. Probably it's best left that way.

~~~~~~

CHAPTER 10

MAINTENANCE OF SOBRIETY
AND GROWTH

To UNDERSTAND MAINTENANCE of an alcoholic's condition of sobriety, one must literally have complete information about how sobriety is brought about. Recovered alcoholics are and always will be alcoholics. As alcoholics — even when recovered — they are surrounded by threats to their continued control of a drinking problem.

In the process of recovery, alcoholics have been coached step by step through the management of the concomitant factors in their sickness. They are many and varied, but fall generally in the classification of occupational and religious factors, limited maturity, deficient education, social and marital problems, and physical disabilities.

The occupational and religious factors are based on the individual's inability to solve moral and ethical problems or to use the talents and skills he believes he possesses. Educational and maturity problems often beset those who have had a great deal of higher education, that is, they have met the academic requirements, but have not applied their learning to life problems and thus continue to behave at times like children. The problem of economic status should be well understood by nonalcoholics. Normal people in a materialistic society are usually more or less content with their economic status. Alcoholics carry their resentment of economic failure or inadequacy into rationalizations and fantasy with liquor.

One may hear accounts of how an alcoholic voluntarily sought help with his illness when a sudden, almost blinding, revelation occurred, but experience proves that alcoholics seldom voluntarily seek treatment and the "revealing" experience is more a crisis than revelation. Coming to treatment, they are always under some form of pressure. They may have attempted self-medication, but will have failed at that. They may have a set of positive rationalizations such as an affirmation that their real problem is excessive drinking or bad luck or a nagging wife or an inadequate husband, but these things do not motivate them to seek help voluntarily. In the vast majority of cases an alcoholic seeking treatment is thrust into treatment by a crisis and appears before the therapist as an unhappy, discouraged, depressed, and egocentric individual.

The alcoholic's first contact interview with treatment will be anything but a candid, truthful account of what has happened to him. He will either distort or deceive about his personal life, moving defensively from one rationalization to another, so that the therapist stalks him through a jungle of deception. Therapists do not seek mastery over the alcoholic. They seek the truth, which alcoholics could, if they were thinking objectively, communicate in a very few minutes.

Once the therapist establishes the true situation, identifying the adverse factors in moral, ethical, educational, economic, marital, social, and physical problems it is then possible to tackle the problems one at a time and finally get around to how to put an end to the compulsive drinking. The complex problem is how to diagnose the causes of an alcoholic's inept management of personal life, then bring him to face the problem of compulsive drinking.

The alcoholic who has succeeded in treatment has first of all learned from personal experience that drinking of any kind is not only undesirable but, by reason of the specific inadequacy to metabolize alcohol, an impossible way of life. Recovered alcoholics have developed a sincere desire to quit drinking once and for all. They have also maintained strict sobriety over a long period of time by working diligently on a personal program of abstinence. They are searching for ways to fill in the gaps left while they were drinking heavily and for ways of improving themselves, their attitudes, and activities to a more acceptable way of life.

Recovering alcoholics are more than ordinarily beset by indirect alcoholic suggestion because we live in a social drinking society. There is literally no refuge from continual reminders of the use of alcohol. Television, movies, books, newspapers, magazines, plays present visual stimulation to an alcoholic. This secondary stimulation of a desire to drink can be more serious than actually being present at a cocktail party where others are drinking.

A recovering alcoholic has usually learned that, while all kinds of drinking threaten, drinking to get over a hangover is even more sinister. The use of alcohol to escape disagreeable thoughts or events lies always in the forefront of an alcoholic's thinking, even though it is counteracted by the knowledge that one drink leads to another. Alcoholics know that nipping is insidious, because of the tendency to increase the size of the drink to the point where the blood-alcohol level gets so high that control is lost. Another threat to sobriety is the retrospective increment in the mind of the use of alcohol for enjoyment, for entertainment, for pleasure at times and places and occasions that may now seem lackluster without alcohol.

The recovering alcoholic will have learned that no matter how bad a situation may be, using alcohol to dissolve it will make it far worse. Actually, any effort to achieve euphoria or contentment by using alcohol has a more drastic effect on the alcoholic than on the average social drinker. Alcoholics generally seek pleasant states of mind in order to rid themselves of unpleasant thoughts related to inferiority, guilt, hostility, rebuffs, disappointments, anxiety, inadequacy, unhappiness, despair. (In consequence they have evaded maturity and have lived in a continuous and almost childish round of excitement, happiness, and irresponsibility.) It takes a long time to reorient one's living to a life of vigorous enthusiasm for the rewards of sobriety, self-discipline, and maturity.

Many times alcoholics ask why they are considered immature, when they are able to function efficiently in responsible jobs and are highly regarded by colleagues as incisive and successful people. The fact is that the greater proportion of humans, equating maturity with age, strive to remain boyish or girlish and excuse or overlook immaturity in others as well as in themselves.

During treatment, many alcoholics find new interests and new enthusiasms which substitute for the irresponsibility of what they once deemed an ideal and satisfying way of life. While they may be disturbed at the outset of treatment by the deprivation of their favorite remedy for boredom, they find a fresh elation in the awakening and stretching of mental "muscles" long disused or abused. They make new discoveries of their mental powers and rejoice in a dawn without a hangover, a night free of insomnia. The emotional instability, which once slashed like the jaws of a predator at anyone or anything that proved an obstacle, gives way to a kind of rueful serenity, in itself so healing that the mea culpa of the testimony in an AA meeting gives a peculiar joy to both speaker and auditor.

The most subtle threat to continued sobriety of an alcoholic is probably the personal prescription of alcohol as a medication, a wish fulfiller always available and quick to grant euphoria. Sobriety is ninety percent actual with the recovered alcoholic, but the other ten percent remains an unspoken hope that sometime, somehow it will be possible to indulge in moderate social drinking. He knows, however, that he must not succumb and actually take a drink. Those who are secure in their recovery do not appear to fear that they either need or will take a drink.

Contemplation of the swift action gained from alcohol in the past exerts a subtle pressure upon behavior. Obviously an alcoholic cannot relapse if he doesn't take a drink, and it is equally obvious that he will not take a drink without thinking about it first. It isn't enough to be able to say with conviction that one does not want to drink again, if the reservation is held "unless some medical discovery or some regeneration of cells makes it possible to drink again."

The tug of the past is strong, not the alcoholic past, but the past of the carefree social drinking days. It is important for the recovered alcoholic to control and direct mental processes when it comes to any question concerning the use of alcohol. Some alcoholics report that they experience "dry" drunks, that is, they have all the feelings that went with drinking in the days before they got sober, but without having taken anything to drink.

Neurologists have long sought for an explanation for the "dry" drunk. In general it is thought to be a subconscious process, in which the feelings registered in the past repeat themselves as in a dream. The recovered alcoholic who experiences a "dry" drunk finds use for the newly gained powers of mental control or redirected willpower.

The fact has been established that the recovered alcoholic who persists in self-discipline and development of maturity gradually wears away the desire or even the fond recollections of social drinking days and that all desire for alcohol disappears. But recovered alcoholics have gained what few nonalcoholics gain from introspection. They have learned a great deal about themselves. And the knowledge has been gained

through striving, as they lived only a drink away from relapse.

The key to maintenance of sobriety is a carefully thought
out therapeutic living program. This is not establishment of
a deadly dull routine which, in most cases, usually results
only in relapse from sheer boredom. Maintenance of sobriety
is, rather, daily attention to constructive improvement of
one's social, economic, spiritual, and creative spheres of interest.

It is sometimes useful to maintain control in alcoholism in
the same way that a diabetic must act to control diabetes. In
fact, the two diseases have much in common in that a strict
dietary regimen must be followed — the diabetic to avoid a
buildup of blood sugar on one hand and insulin shock on the
other. The alcoholic must avoid the buildup of tension and
anxiety on one hand and shun the use of alcohol as a depressant. Both diseases require strict daily attention to the living
program necessary to maintain control.

Recovered alcoholics sometimes find it galling to be in the
position of having to prove themselves over and over again, to
demonstrate that they are *really* in control and not merely
temporarily on the wagon and to explain their abstinence to
the curious and often rude prying of social drinkers, who
demand to know why the alcoholic will not drink with them.

After the first exultant mood from the success of an early
phase of sobriety has passed and the glorious feeling of release from the tyranny of alcohol has settled into a comfortable pattern, alcoholics often experience overconfidence
in their ability to manage their disease. They shadowbox with
the adversary which has landed several knockout punches in
the past, demonstrating their newly agile footwork and fizz
with confidence that they are on the comeback road, stronger
than they ever were. Within limits it is a good and useful
attitude, but when it breeds a decision to sign on for a
championship fight — look out. As boxers say, it's there in the

heart, but the legs just won't obey. A recovered alcoholic must accept the fact that, in such an unequal contest, alcohol will win every time.

Old-timers among recovered alcoholics say privately among themselves that if a recovered alcoholic has to have something to lean on it isn't really recovery, but just a convalescence. But, old-timers who have remained sober for twenty years and longer are also very careful not to lose touch with a therapeutic community of recovered alcoholics — usually to be found in a group of Alcoholics Anonymous.

A few phrases have crept into the language of recovered alcoholics which are useful in setting up guideposts for maintenance of sobriety. That first exultant mood of successful maintenance of sobriety is usually labeled Cloud 9. Coming down off Cloud 9 can mean either relapse or a continuation of maturing management of alcohol problems. This is the time when the recovered alcoholic recognizes that sobriety is not a temporary achievement, automatically propelling the alcoholic into secure management of an alcoholism problem, but that it is something he constantly must reinforce, if he hopes to keep alcoholism isolated and impotent.

Because alcoholics have lived for a long time in a fantasy world of "instant" solutions for all problems, they must establish a means of *not* overburdening themselves with tasks that may put too great a demand upon them. A tolerable average must be found for the daily stresses a recovered alcoholic can take at the outset, and this tolerable average must be raised slowly until he is functioning at the peak potential, which can be very much higher than average non-alcoholics can maintain.

Many recovered alcoholics benefit from the advice given by counselors, members of AA, clergy, physicians, and others concerned in therapy to consciously plan a day's activities. Alcoholics Anonymous has slogans "One Day at a Time," "Easy Does It," "First Things First," and "Live and Let Live."

It warns quite simply not to attempt too much too soon. The experience of many long-recovered alcoholics may be useful. They do not at first seek to project their efforts very far into the future. Some benefit from early rising, making out a limited schedule of things to be done that day without fail, and sticking to that as closely as possible. The items not reached on their agenda are given priority the next day and the next, until scratched off the list.

A talking relationship with other men and women who have the same problem is the best kind of insurance against relapse. During the period of maturing development, alcoholics find their greatest reinforcement in association with others who are following a simple, but vital, daily regimen to control alcoholism. Increasingly large numbers of middle income, middle class, middle aged people in urban areas who are recovered alcoholics search for mutual support in imaginative and practical ways. Very often they form groups within AA groups, segregated into mutual professional or vocational interests. Many luncheon clubs for recovered alcoholics, some called Sahara Clubs, are to be found in such areas as Madison Avenue, Boston's State Street, in San Francisco, in Chicago, and many other cities. This concept of daily get togethers has even been projected into business and industry, where company cafeterias are operated. A corner, nook, or a few tables are set aside for the use of those who find mutual support in controlling an alcohol problem. These same meeting places, in addition to reinforcing AA programs generally, are often used as a means of extending help to other alcoholics not yet under treatment.

The avoidance of boredom and frustration is highly individual and usually requires a patient search for an interest or a hobby. Families often become impatient as alcoholics struggle against boredom, failing to recognize that for a very long time the alcoholic member has been oriented to alcohol and drinking companions, exclusively, for recreation, relaxation, and buffering against tension and anxiety. It must be recognized, however, that alcoholics have been conditioned by their disease to devote most of their waking hours to gratification of their need for solutions, through alcohol, of all sorts of living problems and that something must be substituted to fill the void. In the pat phrase, all their problems are soluble in alcohol.

Filling the void is very often a matter of wise counseling. Most individuals have interests or ambitions which have been unfulfilled, something they have wanted to do and have, for many reasons, never attempted. At the present stage of development of mutual help among alcoholics, the immediate time-filling activity is generally participation in group discussions of the disease or voluntary efforts to help other alcoholics find the means of recovery. These things are not only therapeutic for the recovered alcoholic, but also of enormous assistance to alcoholics in the dawning stages of control of their problem, as well as motivation for those who are denying their problem. But they aren't a raison d'être for fulfilling all the needs of the recovering alcoholic. Often such concentration on the very limited field of alcoholism, and that alone, confines the alcoholic individual to a limited social group.

It is true that, in such limited situations, the recovered alcoholic has easily available talking relationships with people who know what he is talking about and who understand his needs as an individual. Carried to an extreme, however, the limited social group can become another crutch, inhibiting the alcoholic against development in wider areas of social concern.

Regardless of the temptation that may lurk in social situations of broader outlook and wider concern with intellectual, economic, and spiritual welfare, particularly in a social drinking society, the recovered alcoholic must learn to live in this broader social area, successfully managing the rebuffs, the tactlessness, and the ignorance about alcoholism that is encountered in a general society.

The question of explaining why one does not drink looms very much larger in the thinking of recovered alcoholics than its psychological force deserves. Management of this problem depends very largely upon the candor and outgoingness of the individual. Some recovered alcoholics can say bluntly, "I'm an alcoholic. I can't manage the stuff." Some achieve an exquisite tact in which they decline proffered alcohol hospitality, but indicate that they have no rigid ideas against the use of alcohol. Others develop a positive grace in the management of a glass of something that looks like a highball. Some almost drown in tomato juice, orange juice, ginger ale, or quinine water.

Upon reentry into an old social group after a lapse of time, most recovered alcoholics experience a period when their old friends are inordinately curious about their addiction and their recovery. The rule of thumb most useful in satisfying the curiosity of others is the simple dignity of being one's self and giving responsive answers to questions, but volunteering nothing.

This technique of responsive answers and nothing volunteered has the merit of satisfying the curiosity of one's friends and acquaintances, but avoiding the risk of evangelism in the cause of sobriety. The agents of the FBI usually make excellent witnesses in court, seldom talking themselves into trouble, because they give responsive answers. Ask an FBI agent if he has got a match, he will probably say yes, but not produce a match because he hasn't been asked to. Be only as responsive as necessary about discussing one's alcoholism with nonalcoholics and you cannot be labeled as either rude or noncommunicative. Do not hesitate to give information about the disease to someone who asks for it, but don't go around tugging lapels. Education about alcoholism is necessary and vital, but it should be left to the health educators in approaching a mass public.

Recovered alcoholics must learn to accept the fact that the world is peopled by decent, desirable men and women. The world has also, however, a liberal mixture of people who turn off the connection between mind and mouth in situations where ignorance becomes a substitute for intelligence. Learn to live above pettiness, difficult as it may be.

Maintenance of sobriety is, to a great extent, reentry into a competitive society in graduated steps. First there is the isolation of alcoholism, either by rejection or by hostility. The alcoholic first leaves isolation and moves into small groups. Once confidence and self-sufficiency to a limited degree have been gained, the alcoholic should move by carefully measured steps into a larger and more competitive social group. In each social group he must include the professional or vocational group from which he came and to which he aspires.

What may seem to be self-centered and selfish action may take place at this time as life readjustments are made. In cases where family relationships have been drastically upset, the recovered alcoholic must make a sensible determination — always with competent advice — whether to try to reestablish the relationship or whether to make the restorative effort without the pain, tension, and anxiety of seeking a difficult and often impossible reconciliation. In cases of professional and vocational rehabilitation, recovered alcoholics are usually the last to learn that they are not only wanted, but that there is such a shortage of professional and vocational skills they can almost write their own ticket back to normalcy.

Not long ago many employers and many professional groups viewed the alcoholic individual as a dubious risk, and all efforts to rehabilitate were labeled humanitarian projects. Discuss the question today, however, with any practical and enlightened personnel expert, and one learns that rehabilitation of any skill temporarily impaired by alcoholism is a must — a money-saving venture by which the thousands of dollars expended in training and experience are recovered. Geographical escape often is contemplated by recovered alcoholics, even as much as geographical escape is often a device of the active alcoholic. In theory, going elsewhere to start all over again sounds pleasant to the ears of a pioneering people accustomed to seeking new horizons. But, beginning all over again elsewhere, among strangers, is not for the recovered alcoholic in the primary stages of recovery and rehabilitation. He needs every favorable condition to live successfully through the first crucial years of sobriety. One has only to contemplate the enormous difficulties of rehabilitating a homeless, chronic police-case inebriate to give proper weight to the importance of making reentry into society in a favorable community environment. There are also too many stresses and strains in establishing one's self in a new community and in a new social group for the recovered alcoholic to risk unless buffered by friends, relatives, fellow workers, or colleagues. Better by far to fight it out on familiar terrain, where the aids to sobriety are clearly established and available.

The recovered alcoholic who settles for a permanent penance for having been a victim of a disease relinquishes his initiative and growth and continues, for his security, to limit his activities to a small group. There are far too many of them today, subscribing to and reinforcing the tragic fallacy that alcoholics are moral delinquents. Time is mending the attitudes of the general public towards alcoholism and towards the recovered alcoholic. The recovering alcoholic must accept himself and his illness, then move out of his personal sickness, fears, and self-centered interests. It is possible not only to be publicly identified as a recovered alcoholic, but to command respect of the public as well. Several United States Senators and Governors are recovered alcoholics, publicly identified as such without any damage to their careers. Lawyers, doctors, clergymen, professors, diplomats, men and women of great competence in many fields, are recovered alcoholics, and make no secret of it. Personal anonymity is becoming more a concession to the stigma of the disease than a canon of the faithful.

There are no short cuts to stable sobriety for the recovered or recovering alcoholic. Those who press too hard often experience trouble and have to patiently rebuild their control of the disease. Often they depend too little upon themselves and too much upon other people or upon medication. A sound chart does not exist for maintenance of sobriety, setting forth inflexible steps towards security. Indeed, one sees a variation of the progressive symptoms of alcoholism in the period when an alcoholic becomes involved in the struggle with alcohol, and this variation in onset presupposes a like variance in the needs of the recovering alcoholic who is seeking sound procedures.

Some recovered alcoholics do better to change occupations as they achieve sobriety. A salesman who has excelled at selling insurance may find insurance too competitive and demanding on achieving sobriety and switch to selling some less competitive line. Doctors change from one specialty to another during their recovery — often finding an absorbing interest in psychiatry or switching from surgery to internal medicine, prompted by the needs they felt while they were in treatment. One psychiatrist who recovered from alcoholism became a hospital administrator. In the skilled vocations there is not as much change, but often the recovered alcoholic with a skill moves onward and upward into supervision, having gained a tolerance, understanding, and compassion for fellow men which is essential to good leadership.

Recovered alcoholics who pace their lives according to what they can handle, gradually increasing the demands upon their creativity, their tolerance of tension, their management of anxiety, find that they do very well indeed living as carefully as they do. They can compete successfully with the world because the world does not use its abilities effectively. Few people, except those coping with a disease that is controlled by a strict regimen, are under the necessity of planning each day of their lives as carefully as alcoholics.

In marital situations where stress has created almost intolerable dissension between husbands, wives, and children, maintenance of sobriety demands a thorough understanding by all members of the family of the true state of affairs, both before recovery and after recovery.

The most successful family recoveries are a joy to behold. Wives and husbands weather the crisis and afterward share the fruits of victory together. They are equally well informed about alcoholism with its complex symptoms and are fully aware of the dangers that beset sobriety. Children are taught that one or both parents have been ill and are in a period of convalescence. One often hears in therapy a statement from a son or daughter of an alcoholic, "I know that daddy has been ill for several years." Or, in the past tense, "Daddy was ill for a few years, but he's fine now."

For that reason, some consideration must be given during the maintenance of sobriety to full and complete disclosure to family members of the doubts, fears, and rebuffs experienced during the tense periods when sobriety hangs in the balance. It is better to go to extremes, discussing all family matters in the open and in simple unadorned language, than to try to protect the family members from knowledge that a critical situation exists. Very often the reparation of a neglected spiritual life may hinge upon family participation in worship. This does not mean that the recovered alcoholic must necessarily become a rigid pillar of the church. But it can mean that the family life is improved if this often neglected area of personal development is reinforced by church attendance. Clergymen have become essential in providing the psychological support that many alcoholics and their families need to maintain balance and sobriety.

Children who expect and accept support from parents may learn a great deal from the children of a family of a recovered alcoholic which has shared the struggle for stability. Such children take pride in the fact that they have contributed their understanding to solution of a family problem, and they find joy in the achievements of the parent who has struggled to control a devastating sickness.

~~~~~~

CHAPTER 11

HOW TO GET HELP

IF ONE MAKES A DECISION to seek help for an alcoholism problem — for oneself, a family member, a friend, or employee — one must be factual.

Alcoholics and their relatives should disqualify themselves from *interpretation* of what the facts are. They cannot be objective. Alcoholics will go to extremes of self-justification or self-criticism. Relatives are much too close to the problems of alcoholism to gain perspective, and they are too often part of the problem.

At the outset, a necessity is a neutral person or resource to evaluate the facts. The immediate question will be who determines when help is needed. Help is needed when either the person afflicted or those concerned about that person begin to explain away excessive drinking behavior and changes in personality when a person drinks.

When alcoholics become capable of an honest and unsparing personal inventory, they declare without exception that a time came in their drinking history, long before they ever became seriously involved in alcoholism, when they had uneasy feelings about their drinking, when they recognized that they did not drink like others in their social drinking group. Relatives will invariably say that they knew something was wrong from three to five years before they ever entertained a suspicion that the family member was alcoholic. Wives reported in several research projects that they willingly took part in a conspiracy of silence about the drinking problems, attempted to find reasonable explanations other than alcoholic behavior for the husband's drinking problem, and that it was three to five years after they had first observed the drinking excesses that they finally admitted to themselves that their husbands were alcoholics. Even then, they didn't seek help, but continued concealment, withdrew from their social group, tried home "cures," none of which were of any help.

The research findings are borne out by practical experience with alcoholics. Husbands and wives are so busy in attempts to make the drinking behavior of an alcoholic spouse sound normal and reasonable that they do not take the reasonable and sensible action that one would take with any other illness, that is, consult a professional person or a resource that can be of help.

The time to search for a treatment resource is not in the middle of the night when an intoxicated, emotionally upset, and often aggressive alcoholic is raising ructions. It is far better to make up one's mind to seek some help the next day and not to put it off because the alcoholic then will be hung over, repentant, and ready to promise the impossible. The time to call the family doctor is not in the hours when he needs rest, but during regular office hours and with the intention of talking frankly about the problem.

One must be aware that, if the help is sought with the hope and intention of hearing only what one wants to hear and avoiding the unpleasant news that the trouble is alcoholism, it is quite possible to find doctors who will be relieved to dismiss a vexatious problem easily on the basis of the biased information given to them by relatives, even though they may suspect that the real trouble is alcoholism.

Actually, when one seeks help with alcoholism it is with almost certain knowledge that the problem is alcoholism, and, if one has misread the symptoms and signs for any reason, the professionals will soon spot the error, for they are much too busy and overworked to go along with an erroneous diagnosis. Because of moral judgments or bias against the use of intoxicants, don't try to put a stop to simple social drinking by calling it alcoholism.

Finding the most suitable treatment resource for an alcoholic is the crux of the problem in each instance. Facilities differ from community to community and often are as variable as the community's acceptance of the concept that alcoholism is a disease. But certain basic resources can be found everywhere and, when properly approached, will help to locate and enlist the essential service an alcoholic needs.

Taking the treatment step by step, the first and most important consideration is "drying out" the alcoholic so that one can communicate rationally and reasonably with a sick but sober alcoholic. A person who is intoxicated is in no condition to discuss anything with good judgment and calm reason. Therapists experienced in work with alcoholics will never undertake anything with an intoxicated alcoholic but referral to a "drying out" regimen.

It is possible to dry out at home and in the care of one's intimate family or to sweat it out alone and unaided, but the process requires dedication and desperation, acceptance and understanding, cooperation and compassion. Families find themselves yielding to an alcoholic's pleas for a drink to straighten out the toxic condition by raising the blood-alcohol content of the patient but never getting off this deadly carrousel. If an individual is unable to go two or three days without liquor, it is far better to find a hospital bed in a resource that has experience in drying out alcoholics.

Physicians are aware of the location and cost of such resources. One cannot guarantee the results to be achieved by submitting to the sobering up process which so often passes for treatment of alcoholism when it is, in fact, merely an interlude between drinking bouts. Sobering up is only the first step. After that must come treatment which the patient can accept and with which the patient will cooperate.

One should not hesitate to ask questions when seeking effective treatment for alcoholism.

In every community of moderate size, down to the population center of every county in this country, there are low-cost, voluntary public resources devoted to the health and welfare of all. Often several of these services are necessary to bring about control of an alcoholism problem.

Legal, medical, and psychiatric assistance are often free of charge to those who lack the funds, either through legal aid societies, free medical and psychiatric clinics, or services paid for by welfare departments of town, city, county, or state. Social service workers can advise on such referrals.

Tangled finances can be straightened out by appeal to the family service organizations, homemaker services, and friendly visiting services. In the latter case, visiting nurses or public health nurses can often be of great help, not only in suggesting referral sources, but also in home care of alcoholics undergoing a drying out process or withdrawal symptoms or both.

Some may think that financial problems are insoluble and that, because the person responsible for the main support of a family is alcoholic, no one will take an interest or help. The fact is that even mortgagors who have undergone vexatious experiences in delinquent payments from alcoholics will most often accept a reasonable proposal to carry the mortgage or assist in disposing of the property at an advantageous price if they have assurance that the alcoholic individual is trying to cooperate in treatment of alcohol problems.

Homemaking services will cooperate in cases where the homemaker has to go out to work to tide the family over until the alcoholism problem is solved. This includes care of small children who can often be referred to day nurseries or be helped by extracurricular school activities. It is not enough merely to sober up the intoxicated alcoholic and give him the address or telephone number of an AA group, leaving it to chance that the alcoholic's problems will be solved.

The almost universal availability of Alcoholics Anonymous groups in North America and many foreign countries indicates the existence of men and women in every community who have recovered from alcoholism. In the absence in one's community of a physician or a known resource with a developed skill in dealing with alcoholism as a medical or psychiatric problem, it is best to seek out the nearest AA group, attend a meeting or two, and discuss the problem frankly with the people one meets at AA meetings. Nonalcoholics are permitted to attend AA open meetings. It is only the closed meetings at which nonalcoholics are barred.

One should use some care and judgment in choosing the AA member to give advice concerning the individual problem. A rough rule of thumb is that if the AA member has three or four years of sobriety and is not overzealous or didactic about what AA can and cannot do for an alcoholic, one can expect reasonable advice. Each group, moreover, has a secretary with acknowledged stability and sobriety.

If public alcoholism clinics exist in the community, one can expect professional help and effective referral procedures to be available.

One's family physician will be aware of ethical private resources to help alcoholics. But the existence of recovered alcoholics in almost every community provides at least a starting point in the search for effective treatment and counseling for alcoholism.

One should ask for several things from the informant chosen from this group of recovered alcoholics. The first consideration will be a drying-out resource. One can depend upon what the stable AA member says concerning drying out. The group has usually tried all the resources and has learned from experience which ones are good and which are only a means of tapering off from a drunk.

Another prime consideration is to get the names of doctors or psychiatrists who specialize in treatment of alcoholism or who have alcoholic patients in their practice. Conflicting counsel will be given concerning the skills and methods of such professionally competent people, but a great deal of the confusion arises from the motivation, or lack of it, affecting the individual patient. One must recognize that most physicians are not inclined to take on alcoholic patients because (1) they are aware of how difficult an alcoholic patient can be, (2) they are ill informed or only sketchily informed about the disease, (3) they are, from considerations of tact, personal or social relationship, and professional attitudes, reluctant to discuss with a patient what they look upon as a personality disorder outside of their professional sphere. Those physicians who do treat alcoholism carry on a practice covering a wide range of other illnesses. Doctors who give full time to treatment of alcoholism are so rare as to be extraordinary.

The motivation of the alcoholic patient is something which should take priority over everything else. This is often an adroit operation covering a period of months, during which the alcoholic knows little and cares less about the plan to help or is not cognizant of the subtle nature of the effort to create in the alcoholic the desire to accept treatment and get well.

Families, friends, or employers seeking to take appropriate steps to help an alcoholic should first examine themselves and their own attitudes with the aid of a knowledgeable counselor. They should find out how much they actually know about alcoholism and give some time and thought to finding out, not what they think they know about it, but how

little they know about it. This will entail reading useful
literature or pamphlets about the disease. The information
they may get will often be the thread that leads them through
the complex maze of finding the right resources. Only common sense is required to distinguish between outrageous
claims of miracle "cures" and the accurate facts setting forth
the basic information about alcoholism.

Very often a telephone call will start a chain reaction that
will lead to a final solution of alcoholism problems. In general, a discussion of a problem of alcoholism with a recognized
social service agency and specifically with a responsible social
worker or executive of such agencies will provide a starting
point. One has only to ask for the name and address of the
nearest organization specializing in alcoholism to knock at
the right door.

It is recommended that the first action should be to determine whether an information center on alcoholism exists in
one's community. If such a center operates within traveling
distance of one's home, it is important to go to that resource,
explain the problem as it exists, ask for information and
guidance, and then do the necessary homework to tackle the
problem constructively. It may be reassuring to families to
know that by far the greatest percentage of people who seek
help with alcoholism problems are not alcoholics themselves
but relatives, friends, and employers of alcoholics. The actual
treatment of the alcoholic ensues, but this sometimes takes
place weeks later.

It is important to know that in the field of alcoholism the
use of mental health institutions and correctional institutions
as primary resources to help penniless alcoholics is neither
prejudicial or unusual. A period of custodial care or involuntary drying out in such publicly supported resources is
often found in the medical history of many cases of alcoholism. In an emergency these are sometimes the only resources

available, particularly if the patient is undergoing withdrawal symptoms with all the terrifying hallucinations that mark the acute condition called delirium tremens.

There is a consideration, however, which must be weighed — whether the patient is voluntarily committed to such institutions. No accurate studies exist to determine whether the voluntary commitment provides better motivation than the involuntary commitment, but in personal experience those who have entered such resources from personal choice seem better motivated to make the effort to recover than those committed against their will. Yet what must also be considered is that those who wake up and find themselves in custodial care for a period of time reach a crisis in which they become aware of the desperate nature of their sickness and are thus motivated to make the effort to do something more about it than to dry out and wheedle their way to release to resume their drinking cycle. Here is another kink in the complexity of the disease and an indication of the sensitivity of judgments that must be made about an individual case of alcoholism.

Inertia is the greatest handicap that the alcoholic or the person concerned about the alcoholic must overcome. When the alcoholic is intoxicated and troublesome, tension, hostility, and emotion build up to a peak and both patient and those concerned about the patient want something to be done immediately. Once the toxic condition has been alleviated, the immediacy vanishes with the hangover, and the old inertia looks into a rosy optimism that all will be well until the next binge. Thus the first lesson to be learned is that an alcoholic sober is still an alcoholic, just as a diabetic in control of blood sugar is still a diabetic.

In the states or political subdivisions, alcoholism programs paid for by public funds are administered by various departments but usually are under the control of either the State Department of Mental Health or Mental Diseases or the

State Department of Public Health. Inquiry at the state capitol by telephone can elicit this information, and a call with a specific request for referral to the nearest resource under such public programs will provide the needed information.

Although all general hospitals do not provide bed care for alcoholics, most will grant treatment to an alcoholic with a visible injury or with acute symptoms such as delirium tremens. Before entering upon a search for help, it is wise to check with the general hospital in one's home area to determine whether or not treatment is available for alcoholism. Many general hospitals which do not have bed care for alcoholics will have outpatient clinics for treatment, and most mental health centers, both public and private, will provide information, referral, or treatment for some of the many problems arising from alcoholism.

People should not be repelled by the idea of getting help for alcoholism from a mental health resource. For the stability of the alcoholic and for complete understanding of the reasons why alcoholism has become a personal problem, it is often necessary to get professional and scientific attention for the behavioral aspects of the disease. Recovery entails learning why one drinks compulsively as well as how to control the anxieties and tensions common to alcoholics.

One will find the best all-around referral at the voluntary health resources devoted to the information, education, investigation, and control of alcoholism. In the telephone book these are usually listed under the name of the city, county, or area as committees or councils on alcoholism, and virtually all of these voluntary nonprofit organizations are affiliated with a national body — generally the National Council on Alcoholism.

As an example, the Washington, D.C., area Council on Alcoholism takes in part of the States of Virginia and Maryland as well as the District of Columbia. The Greater Boston Council on Alcoholism, the first such voluntary community resource organized in the United States, covers an area much wider than Metropolitan Boston. So, in seeking a telephone number in the phone book, look for city, state, county, or area Councils or Committees on Alcoholism.

If one desires contact with Alcoholics Anonymous, the telephone number is usually listed on the first page of the telephone book. Many AA groups carry ads in weekly newspapers, giving a post office box number and a telephone number.

Similarly, the Al-Anon Family Group, which can be of service to relatives, is listed as such in the telephone book. The listing is usually for a central service office or a special telephone answering service.

One should not be shy or reluctant to discuss the subject with established and qualified resources. Without complete information the help given can be only partially successful. While the general public may still attach some stigma to alcoholism, those working in the remedial field on alcoholism do not stigmatize the disease. They are not interested in who is an alcoholic and who isn't, but in getting proper and acceptable help to alcoholics. Alcoholism happens to all sorts and conditions of people. One can be almost one hundred percent certain that every modern North American is aware of at least one person who suffers from alcoholism. Considering the general acceptability of social drinking, the indifference of the public to the needs of alcoholics is unrealistic. In this enlightened age those who hide the disease can only plead ignorance if they continue to conceal their problem once they have accepted the fact that alcoholism is a sickness.

Alcoholism need not isolate anyone. The lost and lonely need only stretch out a hand to find the firm warm clasp of compassionate and skillful professional help. But such help is not going to seek those who need it and drag them against their will to permanent sobriety. Someone has to ask for the help, to initiate the action. To take the first step, even if one has mistaken excessive drinking for alcoholism, does not brand the individual for whom one is concerned. Those working in the field of alcoholism have far too much to do helping actual alcoholics to waste time trying to convince someone who drinks excessively but not compulsively that he is a victim of alcoholism. But it is wiser to find out which it is and rely upon the judgment of those who are prepared to help.

No alcoholic has ever been helped by having the problem hidden. No alcoholic has ever been helped by pretending that the trouble is something else. The foundation of firm recovery is based on a simple but, oh so difficult, recognition that alcoholism is a disease and must be treated as an illness, and the recovery begins at the point where the alcoholic says, "Yes, it is a disease and I suffer from it."

Step-by-Step Search for Help

If there is a family doctor, request referral or consultation with a professionally qualified physician or counselor.

If there is no medical advice available, look in the telephone directory for any or all of the following listings:

Alcoholics Anonymous (AA)
Al-Anon Family Groups
Committee on Alcoholism (usually named for city, county, or region)
Council on Alcoholism (usually named for city, county, or region)
Division on Alcoholism, Public Health Department
Division on Alcoholism, State Health Department
Clinic on Alcoholism
United Fund, Red Feather, Community Chest (ask for social service)
Family Service Organizations
State Department of Mental Health

Mental Health Clinic
Medical Society, state, city, county, or national

Ask for information about treatment for alcoholism, education and information about alcoholism. It is best to disclose your name and address to these official and voluntary agencies. But if you prefer to remain anonymous, ask how you can make a personal visit to talk the problem over.

In an emergency, keep in mind that for both acute physical and psychological symptoms there are hospital facilities that cannot refuse emergency or first aid treatment. Telephone to your general hospital or have your physician make inquiries concerning bed care for an acutely ill alcoholic.

In communities where hospital resources are denied to alcoholics under that diagnosis, keep in mind that acute gastric symptoms, kidney and liver diseases, stomach ulcers, and any visible injury qualify patients — alcoholic or not — for bed care. It is as dangerous to ignore acute withdrawal symptoms marked by hallucinations, tremors, and convulsions, as it is to ignore a head injury, an internal injury, or a fractured limb. In considering hospital care, one can be assured that few patients with money to pay for hospital care, even for alcoholism, are turned away despite the stigma on the disease which prevails in some communities. The alcoholic without means, however, presents a different problem.

In the latter category consult the local welfare officials, ask the police to take the sick individual into protective custody, or make an effort to have someone with at least some knowledge of alcoholism sit with the sick alcoholic during the acute withdrawal phase. Many alcoholics have strangled from breathing in material regurgitated when nauseated. Members of Alcoholics Anonymous will often help with these acute problems, but AA members cannot be held responsible in a medical emergency. A hospital is the best place for the seriously ill alcoholic. Police are very careful not to leave acutely intoxicated people unattended in a cell or to ignore a visible injury. Many alcoholics have died in police stations in the past, and the police have learned to get medical attention for the intoxicated person as soon as possible.

Seek outpatient care for alcoholics whenever such resources are in your community. Excellent outpatient treatment is available in the states where tax funds support treatment programs for alcoholism. In general, except when acutely ill, alcoholics can undergo treatment as outpatients without interfering with their regular working hours. In fact, the greatest number of present day recoveries are alcoholics who have jobs, careers, families, friends, and homes. Inquire, first of all, for such adjuncts to public health and mental health programs to which everyone is entitled, either free or at a very low cost.

Medical societies in most communities, even to the level of county medical societies, have information about where to go and what to do to get treatment for alcoholism. It is wise to learn who is the best *physician* in your area with particular qualification and seek help from him.

If all the measures have failed to find help locally, write to the following, state your needs, and ask for referral:

The National Council on Alcoholism, Inc.
New York Academy of Medicine Building
2 East 103 Street
New York, New York 10001

North American Association of Alcoholism Programs
323 Dupont Circle Building
Washington, D.C. 20036